CA
Enc

D1554549

Weeds of Colorado

by
Robert L. Zimdahl
Professor, Weed Research Laboratory,
Department of Bioagricultural Sciences and Pest Management

Published by
Cooperative Extension
Colorado State University
Fort Collins, Colorado

Garfield County Libraries

Donated to the
Gordon Cooper
Branch Library

By **EnCana Oil & Gas Inc.**
In support of a project by
Colorado Big Country RC&D Council

Colorado State
University
Cooperative
Extension

GARFIELD COUNTY LIBRARIES
Gordon Cooper Branch Library
76 South 4th Street
Carbondale, CO 81623
(970) 963-2889 – Fax (970) 963-8573
www.garfieldlibraries.org

Acknowlegments

1983 Edition

- Pages 28, 137, 162, and 167. U.S. Department of Agriculture 1970. Selected Weeds of the United States. Agriculture Handbook No. 366. pp. 33, 341, 367, and 423.

The author acknowledges the contributions of those who prepared earlier editions of this bulletin: Thornton, B.J. and L.W. Durrell. 1933. Colorado Weeds. Bulletin 403, Colorado Agric. College, Colorado Experiment Station, 115 pp.; Thornton, B.J. and L.W. Durrell. 1941. Weeds of Colorado. Bulletin 466, Colorado Experiment Station, Colorado State College, 125 pp.; Thornton, B.J. and H.D. Harrington. 1964. Weeds of Colorado. Bulletin 514-S, Agricultural Experiment Station, Colorado State University, 218 pp.; Thornton B.J., H.D. Harrington, and R.L. Zimdahl. 1974. Bulletin 514-S Revised, Experiment Station, Colorado State University, 211 pp.

I express my appreciation for the critical review of Dr. Dieter Wilken, the excellent typing of Mrs. C.L. Wilkins, the editorial assistance of Ms. Elizabeth Bremer, and the artistry of W.L. Stump.

1998 Edition

The contributions of others who created or contributed to previous editions of this publication are affirmed. Mr. Richard G. Walter of Colorado State University's Department of Biology provided essential assistance in modifying the plant key to include species not included in earlier editions. Dr. W.L. Stump prepared the drawings on pages 63, 80, 103, 139 and 189.

Pages 145 and 162 are from U.S. Department of Agriculture 1970. Selected Weeds of the United States. Agriculture Handbook No. 366. pp. 327 and 389.

Table of Contents

"Cursed is the ground for thy sake; in sorrow shalt thou eat of it all the days of thy life; thorns and thistles shall it bring forth to thee; and thou shalt eat the herb of the field."- Genesis 3:17-18

"Weeds are nourished by the same food that would nourish useful plants; and therefore, when allowed to grow along with them, must rob them of part of their food."- Adam Dickson, A treatise on Agriculture 1785

Weeds of Colorado

Robert L. Zimdahl

        In the beginning there were no weeds. Some species have always suc-
ceeded at the expense of others but nature knows no such category as "weed" nor
does nature acknowledge that some plants do not belong. When humans began to
practice agriculture some plants were selected for cultivation and others, deemed
undesirable for food or competitive with crops, became weeds. The Weed Science
Society of Amercia defines a weed as "a plant growing where it is not desired." The
definition is clear but leaves the burden and responsibility for definition with people.
People determine when a particular plant is growing in a place where it is not
desired. Thus, a particular plant is a weed only in terms of a human attitude.
        Weeds interfere with patterns imposed on the environment by humans.
Some weeds interfere with the production of food and fiber; others affect the
quantity or quality of animal products. Some plants are poisonous to humans or farm
animals and others cause human allergies. Weeds harbor insects and pathogens that
can affect crops. Aquatic weeds interfere with navigation and recreation and can
affect production of fish. Some weeds are aesthetic nuisances in lawns and gardens
and along highways, on industrial sites, and utility rights of way.
        Regardless of the location of a perceived weed problem, specific weedy
plants must be identified before one can speak authoritatively about their control.
There may be disagreement about choice of control methods or the need for control
in a particular place. But there is general agreement that weeds are a problem in
many places and this mandates publication of bulletins like this one whose purpose is
to assist in weed identification.
        Many plants found in Colorado could be designated as weeds. However, it is
not possible to include all of them in this bulletin. Therefore, only those plants on
which there is general agreement concerning their "weediness" have been selected.
Even though there is general agreement, there is not universal agreement about when
and where a particular plant is a weed and should be controlled. Some will use this
bulletin to identify a plant so it can be controlled. Others will have an interest in
weeds as components of the environment. Whatever the purpose, the author hopes
this publication will help the reader identify some of Colorado's weedy plants.

CHARACTERISTICS OF WEEDS

        Weeds are plants out of place and defined as such because of a human
attitude about their presence in a certain location. There are few plants that are
always weedy. Although no general definition can be written, the plants generally
considered to be weeds have some characteristics in common that contribute to their
weediness.
        Many weeds are capable of growing under a wide variety of disturbed
climatic and soil conditions. Agricultural fields are good examples of a disturbed
environment; gardens are another example. Weeds are often capable of growing and
reproducing under adverse conditions where crop plants do poorly. Russian thistle's
vigorous growth in dry places or the ability of pigweed to produce seed when mowed
repeatedly are examples of the ability of weeds to grow and prosper in disturbed
environments.
        A single redroot pigweed plant, growing without competition, is capable of
producing in excess of 100,000 seeds. Many weeds produce large numbers of viable

1

seeds and some do so in a short time. The ability to produce many more seeds than necessary for survival of the species is an important factor in weed establishment and spread. Small, inconspicuous seeds often escape notice and are sources of contamination in impure crop seed, while others may be of such size or character as to make their removal from crop seed a very costly, if not impossible, process. The approximate numbers of seeds produced by representative plants, and their comparative size as indicated by the number per pound, are given in the following table.

Table 1. Number of seeds produced per plant and number of seeds per pound for several common weeds. (Source: Stevens 1932, 1957.)

Plant common name	Number of seeds per plant	Number of seeds per pound[a]
Stevens 1932		
Barnyardgrass	7,160[b,c]	324,286
Black nightshade	8,460	197,391
Buckwheat, wild	11,900	64,857
Common cocklebur	440	2,270
Common toadflax	2,280	3,242,857
Dock, curly	29,500	324,286
Dodder, field	16,000[c]	585,806
Field bindweed	50	14,934
Foxtail barley	2,420	403,555
Kochia	14,600	534,118
Common lambsquarters	72,450	648,570
Medic, black	2,350	378,333
Mullein	223,200	5,044,444
Mustard, black	13,400	267,059
Nutsedge, yellow	2,420[d]	2,389,484
Oats, wild	250 [b]	25,913
Pigweed, redroot	117,400 [b]	1,194,737
Plantain, broadleaf	36,150	2,270,000
Prostrate knotweed	6,380	672,593
Purslane	52,300	3,492,308
Ragweed, common	3,380 [b]	114,937
Sandbur	1,110 [b]	67,259
Shepherd's-purse	38,500 [b,c]	4,729,166
Smartweed, Pennsylvania	3,150	126,111
Spurge, leafy	140d	129,714
Stinkgrass	82,100	6,053,333
Sunflower, common	7,200 [b,c]	69,050
Thistle, Canada	680 [b,c]	288,254
Witchgrass	11,400	698,462
Stevens 1957		
Annual bluegrass	2,050	2,270,000
Chicory	4,600	567,500

Common chickweed	600	1,173,127
Common milkweed	600/stem	77,080
Dandelion	12,000	709,375
Prostrate knotweed	4,600	504,444
Redroot pigweed	229,175	1,335,294
Toothed spurge	835	97,634
Velvetleaf	4,300	51,885
Venice mallow	58,600	181,600
Wild radish	1,875	53,412

[a]*Calculated from the weight of 1,000 seeds.*
[b]*Many immature seeds present.*
[c]*Many seeds shattered and lost prior to counting. Stevens, O.A. 1932. The number and weight of seeds produced by weeds. Amer. J. Botany 19:784-794 and Stevens, O.A. 1957. Weights of seeds and numbers per plant. Weeds 5:46-55.*

Seeds of many weed species are comparatively short-lived (2 to 5 years) while others may retain viability for a long time. Curly dock and mullein have germinated after 70 years storage in soil; field bindweed, plantain, and purslane after 40 years; chickweed, foxtail, mustard, and shepherd's-purse after 30 years; redroot pigweed after 25 years; and Canada thistle after 20 years of soil burial. Buried seeds will often germinate when brought to the surface and may thus give rise to weeds in areas that have been kept free of living plants for a number of years.

Dormancy, or dispersal in time, is a characteristic of many weed seeds that permits survival under adverse conditions. The viability reported in the previous paragraph is a function of seed dormancy. Seeds do not all have to germinate when formed, but can wait, suspended in time, dormant, until favorable environmental conditions occur. Although seeds are very efficient means of reproduction, many weeds employ vegetative reproduction as a second reproductive strategy and a means toward greater exploitation of environmental resources. Many plants are capable of propagating themselves by vegetative means such as bulbs, aerial bulbs, bulblets, corms, runners or stolons (horizontal above-ground stems, rooting at the nodes to form new plants), rhizomes (horizontal underground stems), or horizontal roots. Vegetative reproduction is characteristic of many difficult to control weeds.

HARMFUL ASPECTS OF WEEDS

There are many ways in which weeds exact a toll on the plants with which they compete and on the environment. Probably the greatest and most obvious loss caused by weeds results from their competition with crops for light, nutrients, and water. When the quantity of any one of these factors is reduced the crop plant cannot use the others as effectively. The nitrogen, phosphate, and potassium requirement of many common weeds is equal to or higher than that of the desired crops with which they compete. Water is one of the main limiting factors to crop production in Colorado. For example, common lambsquarters and common sunflower require more water to produce a pound of dry matter than corn.

The presence of weed seed in crop seed and harvested products, or weedy material in hay, greatly reduces the value of these products. Grazing or feeding dairy animals weeds such as wild onion can lead to undesirable odors or flavors in dairy products. In production of vegetable or crop seed, presence of related weed species may impair the quality of the seed as a result of cross-pollination.

Weed control requires additional operations and costs: preparation of soil, caring for growing crops, and harvesting. The presence of weeds increases wear and tear on machinery used in growing and harvesting crops and certain pieces of farm equipment are designed and must be maintained for the express purpose of controlling weeds. Serious infestations of noxious perennial weeds may necessitate modification of entire farming programs.

Aquatic weed control is a major problem throughout the world. Weeds growing in irrigation ditches and along ditch banks increase irrigation costs because of the additional expense to remove their growth and accumulated sediment. They also increase water loss through plant transpiration, thus reducing efficiency of waterways. Weeds create problems for navigation on inland waterways and seriously hamper movement in some harbors and rivers. Recreational uses of bodies of water and development of fish and wildlife are reduced by growth of aquatic weeds.

Creeping perennial weeds such as field bindweed and Canada thistle, actually remove land from profitable cultivation each year. Infestations of weeds of this type are a serious menace to surrounding fields. Other weeds, such as the foliar parasite dodder, can eliminate some crops from the rotation, e.g., alfalfa.

Plants such as sandbur, downy bromegrass, and wild barley possess spines or barbed awns that can injure the feet, mouth, and eyes of grazing animals. Plants with barbs and awns are also serious problems in sheep's wool.

Certain poisonous plants may be found growing in cultivated areas where they not only function as weeds, but also constitute a source of livestock poisoning in field or in harvested crops. Poison hemlock may be found along ditches and in other moist places. The seedlings of cocklebur are at times very poisonous, especially to young pigs. Johnsongrass may be extremely poisonous if grazed after being wilted or stunted by drought or frost. Larkspur is one of our most serious range weeds because it is poisonous to cattle.

Victims of weed poisoning or discomfort caused by weeds are not limited to livestock. There have been many instances where children and adults have become ill or have died as a result of eating the roots, fruits, or other parts of poisonous weeds. People also suffer from coming in contact with plants such as poison-ivy. Pollen from sagebrush and ragweed is responsible for hay fever that affects many people every year.

Weeds can increase the incidence of crop insect and disease problems because they harbor the vector. For example, several potato insects live on black nightshade, and the potato leafhopper can live on common lambsquarters and both weeds grow well in potatoes. Potato virus diseases are also transmitted by insects harbored by weeds. Highway departments, utility companies, and railroads spend large amounts of money each year to keep rights of way free of weedy vegetation. Much of this effort is intended to beautify the landscape. In a similar manner, the homeowner, concerned with the aesthetics of lawns and gardens, uses weed control to improve the appearance of the home environment.

THE COST OF WEEDS

In a given environment it may be difficult to measure all costs associated with the presence of weeds. What do weeds cost in a favorite fishing spot or swimming pond? How valuable is weed control in highway beautification or on industrial sites? One measure of weed costs is that associated with use of herbicides in crop production. These costs do not include the costs of commonly employed control methods such as hand weeding or mechanical cultivation. Herbicide production and use have grown more in recent years. than all other pesticides. Herbicides account for about half of all pesticides produced and used in the United States. Their dollar value exceeds that for all other pesticides. Thus, it is not unreasonable to conclude that the crop producer recognizes that weeds reduce profits because of crop competition and, therefore, that their control is profitable. Other U.S. estimates show that uncontrolled weeds are still costing (in reduced yields and profits) several billion dollars per year and that as much as 10 percent of our annual crop production is still lost to weed competition.

CLASSIFICATION OF WEEDS

More than 250,000 plants have been classified. Of these, approximately 300 are grown for food and fiber and more than 2000 are classified as weeds just in the United States. About 150 weeds are legally classified as noxious in one or more states. Colorado classifies 30 weed seeds as noxious and regulates their presence in crop seed offered for sale. For intelligent weed management and control it is important to know the type of plant, its length of life, the time of year it grows and reproduces, and its method of reproduction. These are all important to determine the methods best suited for management and control of a particular species. Weeds are classified in three ways: type of plant, habitat, and life history.

Type of Plant

This is a simple division, on the basis of general structure, into grassy weeds (monocotyledons) or broadleaved weeds (dicotyledons). Other groups such as sedges and ferns are also recognized. This is important knowledge but does not reveal much about any plant.

Habitat

a. Cropland - a diverse selection of many different weeds.
b. Rangeland - includes big sagebrush, gray rabbitbrush, and great plains yucca.
c. Aquatic - plants that grow only in water, e.g., elodea, water hyacinth, cattail, pondweed.

One can also identify species uniquely associated with forest environments and parasitic weeds such as dodder have a unique habitat.

Life History

This convenient and common classification system includes:
a. true annuals
b. winter annuals
c. biennials
d. simple perennials
e. creeping perennials
   1) perennials with aboveground creeping stems (runners, stolons)
   2) perennials with underground creeping stems (rhizomes)
   3) perennials with creeping roots

True Annuals. True annuals, also called summer annuals, germinate in the spring, develop and produce seed during the summer, and die. Plants that germinate in late summer or fall cannot survive the winter, and the growing season is therefore limited to summer months. Examples are common lambsquarters, redroot pigweed, Russian thistle, common cocklebur, and large crabgrass.

Winter Annuals. Winter annuals germinate in late summer or fall and live over winter as small tufts of leaves or rosettes. They resume growth in spring and mature seed early in the summer. These weeds are especially bad in fall-sown grain fields, where mature seed reinfests soil before harvest, and in perennial forage crops such as alfalfa and pasture. Many weeds behave as winter annuals, especially where winters are mild and crop rotations are adapted to winter annuals, e.g., Winter wheat. Winter annuals include shepherd's-purse, prickly lettuce, and downy bromegrass.

Biennials. Biennial plants require two seasons to complete their growth. They grow from seeds in spring and spend the first season storing food, usually in short, fleshy roots; the foliage is limited to clumps of leaves or rosettes. The following season, the plant draws heavily upon stored food and grows vigorously, maturing seeds in summer and fall before dying. Examples are common mallow, common mullein, bull thistle, musk thistle, and common burdock. Ecologists now recognize that triennials, quadrennials, etc. also exist. These are collectively called monocarps and are defined as plants that live vegetatively for a number of years and then bloom and die.

Simple Perennials. Simple perennials possess a root crown that produces new plants year after year. The root crown is supported by a fleshy taproot or a mass of fibrous roots. These perennials depend upon seed production to spread in space, except in the few instances where pieces of the crown may be broken off and are transplanted elsewhere. Examples are chicory, curly dock, dandelion, and broadleaved plantain.

A few weeds of the lily family such as wild onion are known as bulbous perennials and reproduce by means of bulbs, bulblets, or aerial bulblets; seed production often is limited. Modified rhizomes in the form of tubers and nutlets (e.g., yellow nutsedge) also enable vegetative reproduction.

Creeping Perennials. These weeds propagate by seed, creeping aboveground stems, and creeping underground parts. In general, the most difficult to control weeds are found in this group, not only because of their ability to resist control, but because of their constant and relentless spread if left uncontrolled.

Creeping aboveground stems, called runners or stolons, are elongated stems that grow along the surface of the ground, taking root and giving rise to new plants where joints or nodes come in contact with soil. In general, they are not as difficult to control as other types of creeping perennials. Bermudagrass (also has rhizomes), healall, and wedgeleaf fogfruit are examples.

Creeping underground stems or rhizomes possess typical stem structure although they are modified, in some instances almost beyond recognition, by the conditions of subterranean growth. If not too old, they may be recognized by the presence of nodes or joints and small, scale-like leaves. Rhizomes ordinarily grow at shallower depths than horizontal roots, and they may bud. Lateral roots, aerial shoots, and secondary branches always arise at nodes and not adventitiously or irregularly as in horizontal roots.

Creeping or horizontal roots are true roots, characteristically irregular in their growth and lacking nodes and stem structure. They give rise to adventitious aerial shoots and to lateral roots any place along their length. In general, horizontal roots grow deeper than rhizomes, especially in cultivated ground where they may develop some distance below plow depth. They may turn downward at any point and develop as vertical roots. Aerial shoots usually arise at this point and lateral roots continue horizontal growth. Field bindweed, Canada thistle, perennial sowthistle, leafy spurge, and hoary cress are examples of plants that spread by horizontal roots.

Regulatory Classification

The Colorado seed law is a regulatory effort to limit introduction and spread of weeds and to affect their control by regulating weed seed content of crop seed. The law's "noxious" classification is based on existing or potential problems. Weeds classified as "noxious" are especially detrimental and difficult to control.

The law controls weed seed not living plants. It defines a weed as a plant detrimental to agriculture and generally recognized as a weed within the state. The term "noxious weed seed" refers to seed produced from plants that are especially troublesome and detrimental, and that may cause damage or loss to a considerable portion of the land or livestock of a community.

Noxious weed seeds are divided into two classes: "prohibited" and "restricted". A prohibited noxious weed seed is the seed of a perennial, biennial, or annual weed that is highly detrimental and especially difficult to control, and the presence of which prohibits the sale of seeds for planting purposes. They include:

Skeletonleaf bursage	*Ambrosia tomentosa* Nutt.
Woollyleaf bursage	*Ambrosia grayi* (A.Nels.) Shinners
Canada thistle	*Cirsium arvense* (L.) Scop.
Carolina horsenettle	*Solanum carolinense* L.
Silverleaf nightshade	*Solanum elaeagnifolium* Cav.
Field bindweed	*Convolvulus arvensis* L.
Halogeton	*Halogeton glomeratus*(Stephen ex Bieb.) C.A.Mey.
Johnsongrass	*Sorghum halepense* (L.) Pers.
Jointed goatgrass	*Aegilops cylindrica* Host
Musk thistle	*Carduus nutans* L.
Leafy spurge	*Euphorbia esula* L.
Perennial pepperweed	*Lepidium latifolium* L.
Perennial sowthistle	*Sonchus arvensis* L.
Russian knapweed	*Acroptilon repens* L.
Sorghum almum	*Sorghum almum* Parodi
St. Johnswort	*Hypericum perforatum* L.
Hoary cress	*Cardaria draba* (L.) Desv.
Hairy whitetop	*Cardaria pubescens* (C.A.Mey.) Jarmolenko.

Restricted noxious weed seeds are from weeds that are very objectionable in fields, lawns, and gardens of the state, but which can be controlled by good cultural practices. They include:

Black mustard	*Brassica nigra* (L.) W.J.D.Koch
Indian mustard	*Brassica juncea* (L.) Czern. & Coss.
Wild mustard	*Brassica kaber* (DC.) L.C.Wheeler
Blue lettuce	*Lactuca pulchella* (Pursh) DC.
Curly dock	*Rumex crispus* L.
Dodders	*Cuscuta* spp.
Poverty sumpweed	*Iva axillaris* Pursh
Puncturevine	*Tribulus terrestris* L .
Purple groundcherry	*Physalis lobata* Torr.
Quackgrass	Elytrigia repens (L.) Nevski
Wild oat	*Avena fatua* L.

These lists do not include all weeds that may become troublesome after introduction and spread. Therefore such lists will always be subject to change.

The seed law also contains specific label requirements for crop seed for sale. Each container of agricultural, vegetable, or ornamental plant seed that is sold, offered or exposed for sale, bartered, or distributed within the state for seeding purposes shall bear, or have attached in a conspicuous place, a legible and plainly written or printed label in English, giving the following information for agricultural seed:

a. Percentage by weight of all seed, and

b. the name and number per pound of each kind of restricted noxious weed seed present.

In addition, it is unlawful for any person to sell, offer or expose for sale, barter, or distribute within the state any agricultural, vegetable, or ornamental plant seed—

a. Containing more than 2 percent weed seed by weight.

b. Consisting of or containing prohibited noxious weed seed.

c. Consisting of or containing restricted noxious weed seed per pound in excess of the number prescribed by the rules and regulations promulgated under the law or in excess of the number declared on the label attached to the container of seed.

The seed law is administered by the State Department of Agriculture.

INTRODUCTION AND DISSEMINATION OF WEEDS

The first principle of preventive weed control is: use clean seed. The Colorado State Seed Laboratory is maintained at Colorado State University for the express purpose of testing seed purity and germination on a custom basis for any interested party. To ensure against planting weed seed, growers should buy from a reputable dealer and carefully read the label.

Many common weeds are introduced species. New species are constantly being introduced and widespread use of herbicides has often dramatically changed the spectrum of problem weeds because of selective control. Natural agencies, principally human environmental modification, are important in assisting introduction and dissemination of weeds. Weeds often have adaptive characteristics enabling them to fully exploit opportunities for spreading. Knowledge of these adaptive characteristics enable growers to prevent introduction of new weed species and spread of existing ones.

Man, Animals, and Birds

Seed of many plants, such as common burdock, common cocklebur, field sandbur, and hairy beggarticks, have hooks, barbs, or other mechanical means by which they become attached to wool or hair of animals or human clothing and can be transported long distances. Seed of broadleaved plantain, and certain mustards become mucilaginous when wet and can be carried by feet or any part of an animal with which they come in contact. Both animals and birds eat numerous weed seeds, which may pass through digestive tracts intact and viable.

Wind

Strong winds disseminate seed of many kinds, especially over frozen snow. Even breezes and light air currents are effective in dissemination of seed equipped with special devices such as delicate parachutes, tufts of hairs, or membranous wings. Spread of weed seed by wind is usually limited to 2 or 3 miles on average and 10 or 15 miles maximum.

Water

Weed seed may be carried long distances from its place of origin by rain and melting snow. They are carried into rivulets, then into larger streams, and finally into rivers to be eventually washed ashore or deposited in the silt of flooded lands many miles away. Russian thistle was introduced into Colorado near the upper waters of the Arkansas Valley in 1892 and by 1896 had been carried half way across Kansas by the Arkansas River. Not all weed seed floats, but many do, and some (for example, curly dock) have special structures that enable them to stay on top of the water.

Irrigation Systems

Irrigation systems, with their provisions for collecting and distributing water over large areas of land, provide an important avenue for weed-seed distribution. Water has been made much more effective as a result of man's distribution system. Not much can be done by an individual to prevent introduction of weed seed in irrigation water. None of the mechanical devices for removal of weed seed has been entirely satisfactory although many seeds are removed. One of the best control measures, though perhaps most difficult, is to keep canal banks and laterals free of weeds or, at the very least, to keep those weeds present from producing seed. In a series of tests conducted by the Colorado Agricultural Experiment Station, seed of 81 different species of weeds were found to be carried by the irrigation water of the three ditches investigated. It was determined that the number of weed seed passing a given point on a 12-foot ditch during 24 hours may reach several million. It was also found that spring irrigation water is the most heavily laden with weed seed.

Farm Machinery

All types of farm machinery may aid the spread of weeds, especially in wet weather when seeds become attached to implements and vehicles in mud, or by their natural stickiness. Farm trucks may scatter weed seed from their beds. Plows, harrows, and cultivators may drag roots or seed-bearing portions of perennial plants to other parts of a field or into other fields. Combines and hay balers are especially serious offenders, scattering seed from field to field and from farm to farm, sometimes over long distances. Careful farmers insist that all types of itinerant or community equipment such as combines and balers be thoroughly cleaned before being brought on the farm.

Hay and Grain

Hay and grain may be important in weed spread on farms and in areas where livestock raising, feeding, and dairying occur. Many weed seeds pass through the digestive tracts of animals without being injured and may then be scattered on fields in droppings or manure. Weedy straw used for bedding may be a source of field infestation. Viability of weed seed in manure may be largely eliminated by composting manure for 3 to 6 months. Ensiling is also effective in reducing viability.

Common Carriers

Railroads and highway trucks involved in transporting grain, hay, livestock, and other farm commodities scatter many weed seeds along rights of way and highways, which become sources of infestation.

Other Sources

Many weeds have been introduced and distributed with nursery stock; they are carried in packing, in soil around roots, or as associated plants packed with nursery stock. Plants introduced for useful or ornamental purposes have escaped from cultivation to become some of the country's worst weed pests. Bouncingbet, yellow toadflax, matrimonyvine, tansy mustard, chicory, and common dandelion are examples.

WEED CONTROL

Weed control and weed science include work on the selection of cultural, mechanical, biological, and chemical methods to best control weeds in crops and on non-crop lands. Weed science involves far more than answering the difficult question of what chemical will selectively kill weeds in a given crop. Frequently integration of methods is more effective and economical than any one method alone and is nearly always more environmentally friendly. Non-chemical methods of weed control should not be considered as lesser or secondary methods. One of the interesting things about weed control is that, in contrast to other agricultural techniques, no method of weed control has ever been totally discarded. The older methods still have their place and can be combined effectively with newer techniques. Cultivation is among the oldest methods of weed control and is generally a satisfactory method.

Cultivation of annuals may be done many times during the growing season. However, all weeds, whether they be annuals, biennials, or perennials, are more easily and economically killed when they are seedlings. Implements such as the harrow or spring-tine weeder are effective in destroying seedlings, and may be used after crops have been planted and even after they are large. The damage done is usually small compared to the beneficial results derived from destruction of weeds. Deeper cultivation is necessary after annuals, biennials, or simple perennials become established, requiring the use of a disk, spring tooth, sweep, or similar equipment. Intensive cultivation with sweeps or blades, continued over one or more seasons, is effective in controlling creeping perennials.

Mowing is an effective method of preventing formation of seeds by weeds growing in pastures, on ditchbanks, by roadsides, or other areas where cultivation is impractical or impossible. Flowering should not be permitted before mowing, for many weeds possess the ability to mature seed after they have been cut. In some instances, branches will rise from the base of the plant and produce seed unless they are cut off again. Close, frequent mowing to prevent leaf development and replenishment of root reserves may be effective in controlling erect, creeping, perennials, if continued over several seasons.

Grazing serves the same general purpose as mowing, except that it may be more effective if there are enough animals to keep weeds grazed down to the ground. Sheep are especially useful for this purpose.

Burning with diesel oil or propane has a place in controlling weeds along irrigation laterals and in places inaccessible to other techniques. The cost is too high for general weed control. This cost increases greatly as weeds increase in size. Most effective and economical results are obtained when weeds are small. Burning is not effective against established perennial weeds. It has the advantage of immediate observation of results and no residue problems, but the potential for air pollution must be considered.

Control of St. Johnswort and prickly pear by insects illustrates successful application of the principles of biological control to weeds. Although biological control methods are being explored, they are not yet available for most weed problems.

Herbicides for weed control in many different situations have undergone rapid development over the past several years. Available herbicides and use recommendations have changed and will continue to change. No chemical control methods have been included in this publication. Colorado Weed Control recommendations are prepared annually by Colorado State University Cooperative Extension weed specialists in cooperation with other university and industry specialists. These recommendations are current and should be consulted if questions arise concerning specific control problems.

PLANTS POISONOUS TO LIVESTOCK

A partial list of poisonous weeds is included for the reader's information. Losses resulting from animals eating poisonous plants are frequently the consequence of improper range management and overgrazing. Many of the plants are distasteful to livestock and are eaten in harmful amounts only when other forage is lacking.

Weed species

Common name	Scientific name	Animals affected
Western monkshood	Aconitum columbiananum Nutt.	Sheep, horses
Seaside arrowgrass	Triglochin maritima L..	Sheep, cattle
Common cocklebur seedlings	Xanthium strumarium L.	Hogs, cattle, sheep
Meadow deathcamas	Zigadenus venenosus. S. Wats	Sheep, cattle, horses
Brackenfern	Pteridium aquilinum (L.) Kuhn	Cattle, horses,sheep, when fed in hay
Greasewood	Sarcobatus vermiculatus (Hook.) Torr.	Cattle, sheep
Western waterhemlock	Cicuta douglasii (DC.)Coult & Rose	All livestock
Field horsetail	Equisetum arvense L.	Chiefly young horses
Hemp dogbane	Apocynum cannabinum L.	Generally poisonous in large quantities
Timber milkvetch	Astragalus miser Dougl. ex Hook.	Cattle, sheep
Jimsonweed	Datura stramonium L.	Generally poisonous in large quantities
Silky crazyweed	Oxytropis sericea Nutt.ex T&G	Horses
Lambert crazyweed	Oxytropis lambertii Pursh	Horses
Woolly loco	Astragalus mollissimus Torr.	Horses
Low larkspur	Delphinium nuttallianum Pritz. ex Walp.	Cattle, horses
Tall larkspur	Delphinium barbeyi (L.) Huth	Cattle, horses
Lupines	Lupinus spp.	Sheep, other animals at times
Twogrooved milkvetch	Astragalus bisulcatus (Hook.) Gray	Sheep Sheep, cattle
Western whorled milkweed	Asclepias subverticillata L.	Sheep, cattle, horses
Orange sneezeweed	Helenium hoopesii Gray	Sheep, cattle
Poison suckleya	Suckleya suckleyanna (Torr.) Rybd.	Cattle

Mechanical injuries caused by plants are usually due to the presence of sharp awns, burs, heavy spines, or similar structures, and may be in the form of injury to eyes, mouth, tongue, feet, or hide. Lumpy jaw, perforation of the alimentary tract or other internal organs, and an impacted alimentary tract are other forms of distress caused by eating these plants. Such injuries result in loss of weight and in some instances prove fatal, either as a direct result of the injury or through starvation. The following plants can cause mechanical injury to livestock:

Common name	Scientific name
Field sandbur	*Cenchrus incertus* M.A.Curtis
Wild oats	*Avena fatua* L.
Downy bromegrass	*Bromus tectorum* L.
Foxtail barley	*Hordeum jubatum* L.
Common cocklebur	*Xanthium strumarium* L..
Russian thistle	*Salsola iberica* Sennen & Pau
Needle-and-thread grass	*Stipa comata* Trin. and Rupr.

Identification of Weeds

Manuals of this kind can only assist in identification. Because of the large number of weedy species, the variability within a single species, and the difficulty of recognizing weeds at different stages of growth, more specific help in identification may be required. Few people are able to identify all weeds encountered on their land and their only recourse is to send a plant specimen to someone who has more resources and has developed identification skills.

Too frequently, plants are sent for identification without proper care in selecting and packaging the specimen. The plant then arrives in a condition that prohibits proper identification. The following collection guidelines will help to assure that proper identification is obtained.

1. Select a plant that is representative and whole. Do not send just the flower or just the leaves. Good specimens will include leaves, at least a portion of the stem, the intact flower and seed-bearing parts, and part of the underground system. Lack of a complete specimen should not deter one from submitting it, but identification may not be as precise.

2. Unless the plant can be promptly delivered, it should be dried between papers and cardboard placed under a weight. Packing should be sufficiently rigid to prevent shattering in transit.

3. Fresh specimens may be sent in plastic bags or wrapped in aluminum foil but usually are not identifiable, because of decomposition. Decomposition of fresh samples will occur if there is any delay in transit, especially in warm weather.

4. When several plants are submitted, each should bear an identifying tag corresponding to the sender's record.

5. Notes on growth habit, abundance, habitat, and any history of the infestation are often valuable identification aids. The first source of identification assistance should be your county agricultural extension agent. If additional assistance is required, weeds can be submitted to one of the Extension Weed Specialists, Weed Research Laboratory, Department of Bioagricultural Sciences and Pest Management, Colorado State University, Fort Collins, CO 80523. Assistance may be requested from personnel of the Herbarium, Department of Biology, Colorado State University.

BOTANICAL TERMS AND SCIENTIFIC NAMES

In the text, an attempt has been made to keep botanical terms to a minimum. However, it is not possible to adequately describe a plant without use of some botanical terms and scientific names. Most of the terms used are explained in drawings or defined in the text. Special terms employed for grasses are defined and illustrated on pages 20 and 21 and for the Asteraceae on pages 148 and 149.

Common names of weeds vary between regions and within the same region. The common names used herein are those accepted by the terminology committee of the Weed Science Society of America and published in Composite List of Weeds (1989). Other common names are included because of use in Colorado. These may be misleading. Most plants have several common names and the same common name may be applied to two different plants. Therefore, a knowledge of scientific names and binomial nomenclature is essential for proper identification.

Binomial nomenclature is not a system devised to confuse those who want to identify plants. It was originally developed by the Swedish botanist Linnaeus. The "L" following a scientific name means that Linnaeus first named the plant. His system eliminated the practice of naming plants by specifically describing them in Latin.

Scientific names used in this bulletin are applied to plant families, genera, and species. Families may contain several genera. For example, in this book the grass family (Poaceae) contains species selected from the Bromus, Hordeum, Digitaria, and Setaria genera. The genus is a plant group higher than species and includes species resembling each other in some structural characteristics. Scientific names consist of the genus, which is always capitalized, and the species, which is never capitalized. To illustrate that names really mean something the following examples are included:

Wild oat—*Avena fatua* L.

Avena—Latin for oat

fatua—from the Latin fatuas meaning foolish or silly.

Canada thistle—*Cirsium arvense* (L.) Scop.

Cirsium—from the Greek Cirsion meaning a kind of thistle

arvense—from the Latin meaning of the field.

The name for Canada thistle includes the suffix (L.) Scop. Scop. means that J.A. Scopoli modified Linnaeus' original name by transferring the species to a new genus.

The scientific names in this publication originally conformed to the nomenclature in the second edition of the manual of The Plants of Colorado by H.D. Harrington, published in 1964 by Sage Books, Denver, Colorado. As taxonomic knowledge increases plant names are modified. These modifications have been included in each revision.

Descriptions and Illustrations

The following pages contain detailed descriptions and pictures of 171 weed species found in Colorado. An additional 45 species are described but no picture has been included. There are some plants from families with few weedy members. The larger weedy groups such as the grasses begin on page 20 and the many broadleaved species begin on page 51. A simple identification key begins on page 193. An index of plant families is on page 213 and an index to the weed species is on page 215.

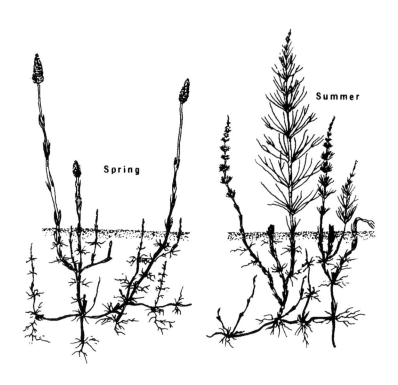

Spring

Summer

FIELD HORSETAIL, horsetail, scouring rush (*Equisetum arvense* L.). Horsetail family. Native. Perennial. Horsetail reproduces by spores rather than true seeds and by creeping, tuber-bearing rootstocks. Annual aboveground growth is dimorphic (of two kinds). The first appears in spring as close growing, erect, hollow, jointed, unbranched fertile or fruiting stem, 1/8 to 1/4 inch in diameter and 4 to 12 inches high, without chlorophyll. It is terminated by a spore-bearing cone, 3/4 to 1 1/2 inches long. Each joint of the stem is surrounded by a slightly inflated pale to brownish sheath 1/4 to 1/2 inch long terminating in dark teeth with a clear margin. These stems mature and wither early. The sterile, vegetative stem arises after the fertile stem (they are often seen together). These are green, 1 to 2 feet tall, hollow, and less rugged. They are sometimes prostrate but usually upright with short joints and radial clusters (whorls) of slender, three- to four-angled smooth branches (often with silica tubercles), 4 to 6 inches long at each joint, giving the plant the appearance responsible for its common name. Leaves are reduced to sheaths around the stem between the branches. Each sheath is green to blackish, with persistent, brown to black lanceolate teeth surrounding the easily separable joints of the stem. The plant has a high silica content, and the presence of an alkaloid renders it poisonous, mainly to horses, and therefore it is an undesirable constituent of hay. It occurs as a weed along streams and ditches and in hay meadows and fields where moisture is favorable. It may serve as a soil binder, especially on ditch banks, but also may be an undesirable weed which is found scattered over Colorado up to 10,500 feet.

SEASIDE ARROWGRASS, arrowgrass (*Triglochin maritimum* L. var. *elata* (Nutt.) A. Gray). Arrowgrass family. Native. Perennial. Seaside arrowgrass reproduces by seed and short, stout rhizomes. It forms scattered clumps or sometimes patches. Leaves are basal with membranous sheaths and are grasslike but thick and half round instead of flat. Leaves are narrow and 6 to 12 or more inches long. The flowering stems are 1 to 4 feet tall and the raceme grows up to 15 inches long. Inflorescences are erect, straight or irregularly twisted. Each flower has 6-petals, and is small, green, and inconspicuous. The fruit is slender, about 1/2 inch long and divides into six sections each bearing a single seed. Seaside arrowgrass grows in damp soil in pastures and hay meadows. It contains hydrocyanic acid and has caused serious livestock losses, when eaten green or especially when fed in hay. It is widely distributed in the western states and scattered over Colorado from 4,500 to 8,500 feet.

WATER SEDGE, bullgrass, ripgut grass (*Carex aquatilis* Wahlenb.). Sedge family. This native tufted perennial, reproduces by seed and from a long, brown root stock. It can have weak stolons. It exhibits grasslike growth with the culms growing 1 to 3 feet tall. Culms are triangular above and slender and red at the base. Leaves are narrow, tough, 1/5 to 1/3 inch wide, usually growing taller than the stems and they are rough near the end. There are one to three terminal male spikes each 1 to 2 inches long. Two to six female lateral spikes are cylindrical, 1 to 3 inches long, about 1/5 inch in diameter, densely flowered and vary in color from yellow-green to purple or black or a combination of these colors. Achenes are encased in a flattened membrane and are 1/12 to 1/6 inch long. It grows along irrigation and drainage ditches and reduces flow by narrowing ditches and by trailing numerous long leaves in the water. The tough, intertwining, matted rootstocks are difficult to remove. Sometimes it may be valuable in preventing washing of ditch banks. It is scattered in Colorado except for the west from 5,000 to 11,000 feet.

YELLOW NUTSEDGE, yellow nutgrass, chufa *(Cyperus esculentus* L.). Sedge family. A creeping perennial that reproduces by seed and nutlike, 1/2 to 3/4 inch long edible tubers (nutlets) borne at the ends of slender, scaly rhizomes. Stems are smooth, erect, acutely triangular, yellow-green, pithy, and 6 to 30 inches tall. True leaves originate at the stem base are about the same length as stems and are triangular, narrow, and ribbon-like with roughened edges and a shiny or waxy surface. Involucral, leaf-like bracts, longer than the inflorescence radiate out from the base of the floral cluster. Inflorescences are yellow-brown compound umbels, with several unequal unequal rays. Each ray or spike of the inflorescence has numerous, crowded spikelets each with 8 to 30 flowers. Achenes are yellow-brown, oblong, three-angled, about 1/8 inch long. It grows in moist places and may become established in lowland meadows or irrigated cultivated fields where it is difficult to control because of the persistent tubers. It is present but not widespread in Colorado.

GRASS FAMILY- POACEAE

The grass family, by virtue of its wide distribution, environmental adaptability, numerous species, and patterns of growth, has greater economic importance than any other plant family. Several grasses are important crops (e.g., wheat, barley, corn, rice) while others are serious weeds.

Grasses possess unique structures that have special descriptive terms, necessary to describe the species. The illustration on page 21 is an attempt to clarify the special terms used in the text. Grasses are annual or perennial. Many of the perennials possess rhizomes, creeping underground stems. Stems of grasses are usually hollow except at the conspicuous nodes or joints. Leaves are solitary at nodes and are arranged in two ranks on the stem. Each leaf has two distinct parts: the sheath, which forms a tube about the stem, and the blade, a long, narrow, non-clasping and usually flat part of the leaf. At the junction of sheath and blade there is a membranous or hairy outgrowth, the ligule. Auricles, clawlike projections at the base of the blade, are present in some grasses.

Grass flowers lack petals and sepals and consist of three stamens and a single ovary surmounted by two feathery stigmas. So similar are the flowers from species to species that identification often must depend on the manner in which the flowers are grouped and on the structure, texture, and presence or absence of flower parts.

Typically, each individual grass flower is enclosed between two scales or bracts. One of these, the lemma, is usually larger and frequently encloses the other, the palea. The lemma, palea, and enclosed flower are called the floret. Florets are arranged in spikelets. Each spikelet typically consists of two glumes within which are one or more florets.

Spikelets are arranged in various ways. In some grasses such as wheat or rye, the spikelets are sessile along the flowering stem and together form a head. In oats, spikelets are arranged in a loose branched inflorescence known as a panicle.

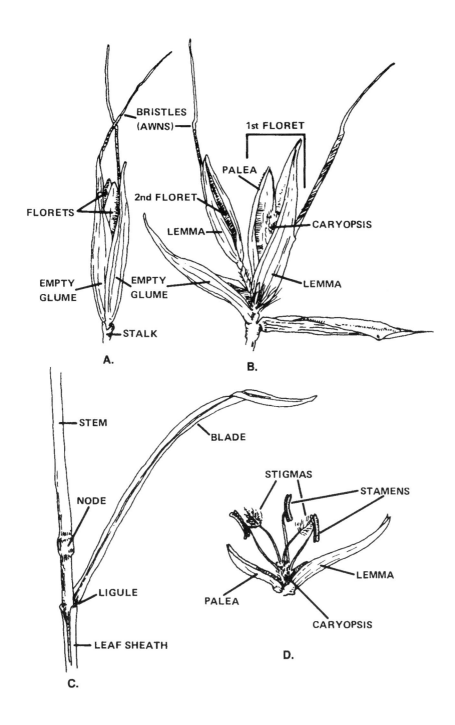

A. Spikelet of wild oats; B. Spikelet with empty glumes bent back to show the floret (diagrammatic); C. Grass leaf and part of stem; D. A single floret (diagrammatic).

ALTA FESCUE, tall fescue, reed fescue, coarse fescue (*Festuca arundinacea* Schreb.). Grass family. Fescue tribe. A perennial bunch grass introduced from Europe. The stems are 2 to 4 feet tall and usually grow in mats or clumps but the plant may be rhizomatous. The upper surface of the numerous, flat to somewhat rolled, narrow leaf blades is rough to touch. Leaves are 2 to 18 inches long and less than 1 inch wide. Ligules are collar-like and the prominent auricles have ciliated (fringed with hairs) margins. Panicles are erect, 4 to 12 inches long, and open after flowering. Spikelets are usually three - to six-flowered. It is found in meadows, pastures, and roadsides and is a serious weed in turf. It was introduced from Europe as a forage plant. Tall fescue is commonly confused with meadow fescue (F. pratensis) to which it is very similar except that Alta fescue is larger and its prominent auricles have ciliated margins and meadow fescue's do not.

ANNUAL BLUEGRASS *(Poa annua* L.). Grass family. Fescue tribe. This introduced annual from Europe reproduces by seed. In contrast to the implication of its scientific name, that it is only an annual, it can be an annual (variety *annua*) or a short-lived perennial (variety *reptans*). Its tufted stems are 2 to 12 inches high and sometimes root at lower nodes. The leaf blades are soft, bright green, about 1/8 inch wide and 1 to 4 inches long with a curved, prow-like tip. The ligule is membranous, thin, white, and less than 1/2 inch tall. The pyramidal, open panicle ranges from 1 to 4 inches long with small spikelets each 1/5 inch long, with 2 to four (sometimes 6) seed-bearing florets. Lemmas are overlapping and each has five nerves. Bright amber seeds (caryopsis) are very small, dorsally keeled and pointed at both ends. Annual bluegrass grows in gardens and is an important weed in golf course, cemetery and other turf areas where it makes a compact, undesirable, continuously flowering, matlike growth in spring and early summer and dies early, leaving unsightly dry, brown areas. It is widely distributed over Colorado from 5,000 to 9,500 feet.

DOWNY BROME, downy bromegrass, downy chess, early cheatgrass (*Bromus tectorum* L.). Grass family. Fescue tribe. An annual or winter annual introduced from the Mediterranean area of Europe and first found in the US near Denver, CO. It is probably the most common plant species in the intermountain west area dominating over 100 million acres. It reproduces by seed and has smooth, slender, erect stems, 4 inches to 2 1/2 feet tall. Leaves and sheaths and flat blades are densely covered with soft hairs, flat, 2 to 6 inches long. Panicle are 2 to 6 inches long with slender branches that droop to one side. It has numerous, five- to eight-flowered spikelets with slender, straight awns 3/8 to 5/8 inch long that are purple at maturity. Each awn is attached to the lower lemma of the hairy, buff-brown, 1/2 inch long, narrow seed. Mature plants are red-brown in color. It is a strong invader and creates a serious fire hazard after it matures in late spring. It can be a desirable spring forage plant for about 6 weeks in pastures, on rangelands and along road sides. It is widely distributed in Colorado from 4,000 to 9,000 feet and many be the most common plant species in the western U. S.

CHEAT, chess (*Bromus secalinus* L.). Grass family. Fescue tribe. This introduced annual has erect, smooth, 1 to 2 1/2 foot tall stems. The leaf sheaths and blades are smooth to somewhat hairy. Sparsely hairy leaf blades are 1/8 to over 1/4 inch wide, and 3 to 10 inches long. Its open panicle is 3 to 4 inches long with branches that droop at maturity. Each branch bears two to three rather compact spikelets, 1/2 to 3/4 inch long, each with 6 to 10 seed-producing florets, with short awns. The seed (caryopsis) is about 1/4 inch long, smooth, deeply grooved and orange-brown. Lemma margins are deeply in-rolled at maturity. It is a serious weed in small grains and is common in Colorado.

SALTGRASS, inland saltgrass [*Distichlis picata* (L.) Greene subsp. *stricta* (Torr.)]. Grass family. Fescue tribe. A low-growing, mat-forming, native, creeping perennial that reproduces by seeds and extensive, scaly, horizontal rhizomes, and frequently forms a compact cover. The stems are smooth, 4 inches to 1 1/2 foot tall, stiffly erect or reclining, with ascending ends. Stems root at nodes to form new plants. It has numerous, spreading alternate leaves that come up the stem in two rows. Each leaf is up to 1/8 inch wide, and 1/2 to 4 inches long, flat or rolled inward and tapered at maturity. The ligule is a short fringed membrane often flanked by long hairs and with long hairs behind it. There are no auricles. Plants are dioecious with male and female flowers on separate plants; male spikelets are smaller and flatter. Flowers are flattened spikelets clustered at the top of stems. The seeds are dull, light brown, oval, about 1/16 inch long, with a two-pronged beak. It has little forage value, and is grazed when it is the only available grass. Saltgrass most often grows in alkaline moist soils, frequently along river bottoms and edges of lakes, sometimes in fields. It is widely distributed in Colorado from 3,500 to 9,000 feet.

25

STINKGRASS, lovegrass, candygrass [*Eragrostis cilianensis* (All.) E.Mosher] Grass family. Fescue tribe. An introduced tufted, annual that reproduces by seed. The name is derived from small glands on foliage and spikelets that exude a disagreeable odor. It has smooth, erect, hollow or pith filled stems that are decumbent at the base but bend upwards and grow 6 inches to 2 feet tall. Leaf sheaths are shorter than the internode and smooth but often have a line or tuft of long hairs at the collar. The blades are 2 to 6+ inches long, about 1/4 inch wide, flat, and smooth beneath. The panicles are 2 to 9 inches long with short spreading or ascending branches each 1 to 2 inches long, densely flowered, and gray-green in color. Its spikelets are variable with 8- to 35-flowered (occasionally less), closely imbricated florets. Seed shatters readily when mature and is very small (1/30 inch long), egg-shaped, red-brown. It is offensive to livestock both as green forage and hay. Stinkgrass grows in hay, pastures, alfalfa, and on dry land in most parts of the U. S. In Colorado it is most commonly found in the eastern half from 4,000 to 9,500 feet.

26

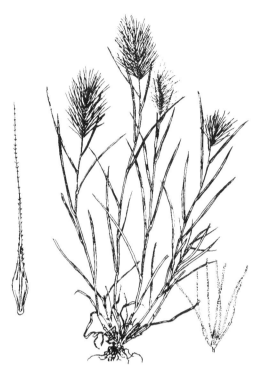

FOXTAIL BARLEY, wild barley *(Hordeum jubatum* L.). Grass family. Barley tribe. A native, thickly tufted or bunched perennial. Stems are smooth, up to 2 feet tall, erect, and sometimes decumbent at base. The leaf sheaths are smooth, loose, shorter than the internodes with erect, rough, 2 to 5 inches long, narrow, flat, gray-green blades. Its pale-green, bushy, nodding, spike inflorescence is 2 to 4 inches long, nodding, with spreading, slender, barbed awns each 1 to 1 1/2 inches long. Auricles are absent. The inflorescence is 3 to 5 inches tall, including awns and is often partially included in the uppermost leaf sheath. When mature the inflorescence breaks into 7-awned clusters of one fertile and two sterile spikelets. Seed is yellow, hairy at the tip, and about 1/8 inch long. It is injurious to livestock because the barbed awns pierce the gums and tongue, causing ulcerations and swellings. It grows on any soil, wet or dry, in fields, meadows, and pastures, and is widely distributed over Colorado from 3,400 to 10,000 feet.

LITTLE BARLEY (*Hordeum pusillum* Nutt.). Grass family. Barley tribe. This native, tufted or solitary stemmed annual sometimes behaves as a winter annual. It is similar to foxtail barley but usually much smaller. Stems are 4 to 12 inches high with 1/2 to 3 inch long leaves that are frequently densely pubescent. Flowering heads are smaller than foxtail barley, compact, 1 to 3 inches long, with short, stiff, smooth awns, about 1/2 inch long. The seeds are similar to foxtail barley but larger. It appears early in spring, but soon becomes unpalatable. Its presence is evidence of serious overgrazing and it is widely distributed over Colorado from 3,400 to 6,500 feet.

SQUIRRELTAIL [*Elymus elymoides* (Rafin.) Swezey] = [Sitanion hystrix (Nutt.) J.G.Sm]. Grass family. Barley tribe. A related perennial with an open, bilateral spike inflorescence and long, finely barbed awns. The spike breaks into segments at maturity and spikelets of each node fall attached to the internode below.

27

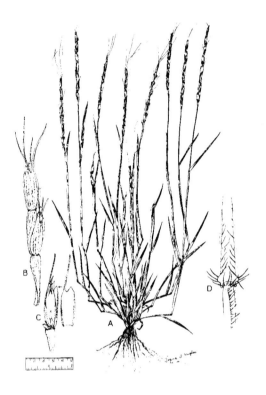

JOINTED GOATGRASS *(Aegilops cylindrica* Host). Noxious. Grass family. Barley tribe. Jointed goatgrass behaves as a winter annual in Colorado. It probably was introduced to the United States in wheat from Turkey in the late 1800's and spread rapidly in grain growing areas. It grows 15 to 30 inches tall in erect stems or tillers that branch at the base to give the plant a tufted appearance. The leaf blades are flat, 1/8 to 1/4 inch wide (usually smooth but may be hairy). Auricles are inconspicuous to absent. The ligule is a fringe of hairs. The root system is shallow and fibrous. The most distinguishing characteristic is the 2 to 4 inch cylindrical, balanced spike. The spike has rarely two and up to 10 or more two- to three-flowered (infrequently five) hairless spikelets. Each spikelet is about 1 inch long, and they are tightly arranged alternately each slightly longer than the internode of the rachis. Spikelets most commonly contain two fertile florets and one reduced nonfertile floret. Glumes are several nerved with a keel on one side that extends into a single awn. The lemma slightly exceeds the glumes and has several harsh awns which give the entire head a bearded appearance. At maturity spikes fall intact and spikelets separate with a segment of the rachis still attached. Seed is about 3/16 inch long, bearded at one end and resembles a wheat grain. Seed is shed in June and July during and prior to wheat harvest. It is common in dryland areas of Eastern Colorado.

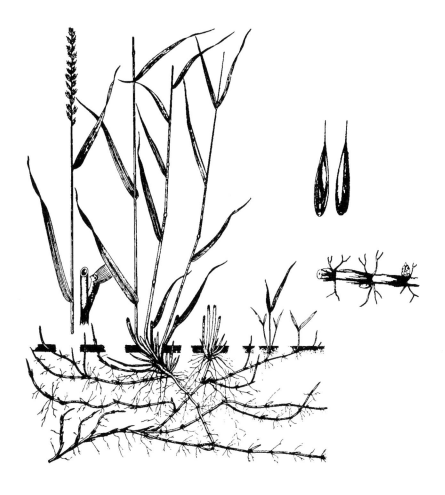

QUACKGRASS, couchgrass [*Elytrigia repens* (L.) Nevski. formerly *Agropyron repens* L.]. Noxious. Grass family. Barley tribe. This creeping perennial was introduced from Europe and grows well in moist soil in cool, temperate areas. It reproduces by seed and by long, slender, jointed, straw-colored, usually pointed rhizomes that form a shallow, dense mat in soil. Slender, hollow stems are erect, 1 to 3 feet tall, with narrow leaves that are rough above and smooth beneath. Small auricles are found at the junction of leaf blade and sheath. Leaves often have a sharp constriction below the tip. Seeds are straw-yellow, narrow, up to 3/8 inch long, with short awns. They are borne on spikes that are 2 to 6 inches long and resemble slender heads of wheat. It can be a good pasture grass and may be used for hay, but under most conditions it becomes weedy. It is generally distributed throughout the United States except in the South. It is not a very important weed in agronomic crops in Colorado but can be found from 4,500 to 9,000 feet.

WILD OAT *(Avena fatua* L.). Noxious. Grass family. Oat tribe. An annual introduced from Europe or Asia that reproduces by seeds that may remain viable in soil for a few years (in Colorado), making it difficult to eradicate. It is similar in appearance to tame oats *(A. sativa)* but usually grows taller and has a more open 4 to 12 inch long panicle. Hollow culms grow 1 to 4 feet tall. Leaf blades are flat, 1/8 to 5/8 inch wide with open sheaths and a membranous ligule but no auricles. Panicle spikelets have 2 to 3 florets that disarticulate above the glumes. Seed is yellow to almost black, narrowly oval, 1/4 to 1/2 inch long and can be distinguished from tame oat seed by the twisted awn which bends at right angles and a horseshoe-shaped scar or "sucker-mouth" at its base, which is surrounded by stiff brown hairs. It grows in cultivated fields and is especially troublesome in spring grain crops. It is found throughout the state from 3,500 to 9,500 feet.

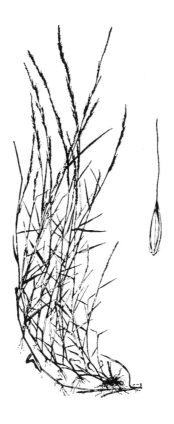

NIMBLEWILL (*Muhlenbergia schreberi* J.F.Gmel.). Grass family. Bentgrass tribe. This introduced erect to sprawling perennial reproduces by seed and does not form creeping rhizomes. It has slender, branching, spreading, erect early and later decumbent stems that root at lower nodes and are up to 2 feet long. The leaf sheaths are loose, smooth, and usually pubescent on the margins near the collar. Flat leaf blades are rough, narrow and up to 4 inches long. They are often pubescent near the collar. Flowering stems may arise from rooting nodes and are 4 to 12 inches tall, with slender, loosely-flowered, nodding panicles each 2 to 6 inches long. Seed is brown and very small. It grows in damp shady places in pastures and waste places and may be troublesome as a lawn weed. It is present but not common in Colorado.

CREEPING BENT, redtop (*Agrostis stolonifera* L.) Grass family. Bentgrass tribe. This is a native low-growing, creeping strongly to weakly rhizomatous perennial that reproduces by seed and vegetatively. Variety *A. major* (Gaud.) Farw. has open panicles and is strongly rhizomatous with weak stolons, whereas variety *A. stolonifera* is weakly rhizomatous and strongly stoloniferous. The variety *A. palustris* Huds. Farw. has condensed panicles and is strongly stoloniferous and roots at stem nodes. Culms are erect but commonly decumbent and root at the base. They grow 8 to 20 inches high if unmowed. The flat leaf blades are about 1/8 inch wide and 1 to 4 inches long. Ligules are membranous, thin, 1/32 to 1/8 inch high and entire or finely toothed. The 2 to 5 inch red to purple panicle is closed most of the season but opens when flowering. The grass is used for lawns and for putting greens on golf courses, but is a weed in bluegrass lawns. It is found throughout Colorado from 4,500 to 8,500 feet.

BERMUDAGRASS, devilgrass [Cynodon dactylon (L.) Pers.] Grass family. Windmillgrass tribe. A creeping perennial probably introduced from Africa that reproduces by seed, by extensive, wiry, flattened stolons that root at the nodes, and by long, tough, scaly, highly branched rhizomes that grow at various depths to form a dense sod. Leaf blades are 1 to 4 inches long, narrow, flat, stiff, and smooth except for a conspicuous ring of marginal hairs at the junction of leaf blade and sheath. Ligules are short and obviously fringed. Leaves are rolled in the bud and loosely folded inward at maturity. Seed-bearing stems are decumbent below, usually hollow. Erect culms are leafy and 5 to 17 inches tall with a terminal cluster of 3 to 7 one-sided spikes each 2 to 3 inches long and radiating "fingerlike" from a single whorl at the stem end. Each spike is 1 to 2 inches long with two rows of sessile spikelets on one side of the flattened rachis. Seeds are narrow oval, orange-red to straw-colored, about 1/16 inch long. It is a valuable grass in the South for lawns, pastures, and soil binding, but is a serious pest in cultivated fields. It grows in cultivated fields, pastures, and lawns in Colorado. Because the panicles are similar, it is often confused with the annual - crabgrass (page 38).

WINDMILLGRASS (Chloris verticillata Nutt.). Grass family. Windmillgrass tribe. This, non-rhizomatous perennial reproduces by seed. The stems are 4 to 16 inches tall with several occurring in a close cluster and they are erect or sometimes decumbent at the base and root at the nodes. The leaf blades are narrow, 1 to 3 inches long, flat or folded, with smooth or rough surfaces. Leaf sheaths are keeled with smooth thin, dry margins. There are 6 to 20 seed bearing spikes, each 3 to 6 inches long and in one to three whorls on the stem. These break off at maturity and tumble with the wind. The seeds are light brown, narrow, about 1/4 inch long and awned. Windmillgrass grows on the eastern plains, in cultivated fields, and on roadsides throughout Colorado.

WINDMILLGRASS

BERMUDAGRASS

REED CANARYGRASS *(Phalaris arundinacea* L.). Grass family. Canarygrass tribe. An introduced perennial that reproduces by seed and stout creeping rhizomes. Stems are 2 to 7 feet tall with a waxy surface coating that makes leaves look blue-green. Leaves are 1/4 to 3/4 inch wide, 4 to 12 inches long, and smooth. Edges of leaf tips are often rough to touch. Immature panicles are 3 to 6 inches long, narrow, dense, spikelike, reddish tinged during anthesis but becoming straw-colored and open when mature. All spikelets have one perfect, larger central floret and one or two sterile florets. Reed canarygrass grows in marshes, river banks, and wet meadows and can be a problem in irrigation ditches. It is found mainly in the western two-thirds of Colorado below 9,000 feet.

BARNYARDGRASS, watergrass [*Echinochloa crus-galli* (L.) Beauv.]. Grass family. Panicgrass tribe. Barnyardgrass an aggressive annual introduced from Europe reproduces by seed. It has a stout, smooth 8 inch to 5 foot high stem that often branches basally and is usually reddish to purple at the base. Leaf sheaths are somewhat compressed, smooth and keeled. Blades are 4 to 12 inches long, 1/4 to 3/4 inch wide and smooth. There is neither ligule nor auricles but there are often marginal hairs in pustules in the collar region. The large often red to purple 2 to 10 inch long panicle is composed of 5 to 15 sessile, erect or spreading branches. Each short-awned, bristly-hairy spikelet is one-flowered, green or purple, and they are densely crowded in two to four irregular rows on one side of the rachis. Primary (lowermost) panicle branches have bristles that may be longer than the spikelets. Seed is oval, pointed, smooth, tan to brown and 1/8 inch long. Barnyardgrass is common over the state at altitudes up to 7,500 feet.

GREEN FOXTAIL, pigeongrass, bristlegrass, wild millet [*Setaria viridis* (L.) Beauv.].
Grass family. Panicgrass tribe. Green foxtail, an annual introduced from Eurasia,
reproduces by seed. The erect, hollow stem is often bent basally but grows 8 inches
to 2 feet tall and is simple or branched. Somewhat keeled leaf sheaths are smooth
but rough-margined blades are 2 to 10 inches long. The ligule is a fringe of hairs
from a short membranous base. Each cylindrical inflorescence is erect or nodding, 1
to 4 inches long, and crowded with spikelets. Each spikelet is subtended by 2 to 6
green or yellow-green bristles each nearly 1/2 inch long, giving the head a fuzzy
appearance and the plant's common name - foxtail. Seeds are narrowly oval, green
to yellow to light brown, finely roughened, and about 1/16 inch long. It grows in
cultivated soils throughout the United States and is very common in Colorado up to
8,500 feet.

YELLOW FOXTAIL, pigeongrass, bristlegrass, wild millet [*Setaria glauca* (L.) Beauv.].
Grass family. Panicgrass tribe. A tufted annual, introduced from Eurasia that reproduces by seeds. Erect stems branch from the base and usually grow erect from 1 to 3
feet tall. The leaf sheaths are smooth, 2 to 8 inches long, 1/2 inch wide, and flat.
Leaf blades are smooth, 1/8 to 3/8 inch wide with distinct, long hairs on the margin
near the leaf base (See picture). Green foxtail does not have similar hairs. The ligule
is a fringe of hairs from a short membranous base. Cylindrical panicles are 1 to 4
inches long, blunt, with each crowded spikelet subtended by 6 to 10 long, yellowish-
brown or orange bristles, giving the spike a fuzzy appearance. Seeds are broadly
oval, green to yellow to dark brown, coarsely roughened and about 1/8 inch long.
Seeds are larger than those of green foxtail. It grows in cultivated areas and is less
common than green foxtail in Colorado.

BRISTLY FOXTAIL, bur bristlegrass [*Setaria verticillata* (L.) Beauv.] Grass family.
Panicgrass tribe. This annual weed is very similar to green foxtail. It grows 1 to 3
feet tall. The character that distinguishes it from green foxtail is its segmented
inflorescence. Stiff, rough spikelet bristles remain attached to the rachis after seeds
fall and the bristles are downwardly barbed and adhere to objects or fur.

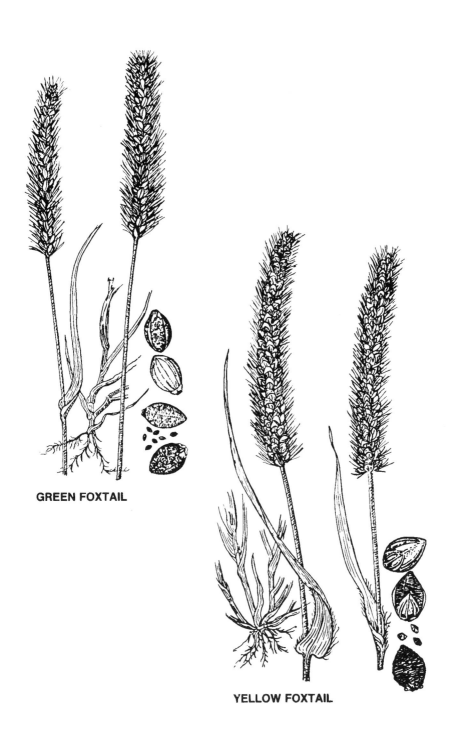

GREEN FOXTAIL

YELLOW FOXTAIL

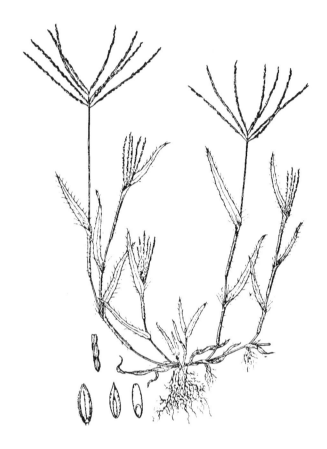

LARGE CRABGRASS, hairy crabgrass, purple crabgrass [*Digitaria sanguinalis* L.) Scop.]. Grass family. Panicgrass tribe. This annual, introduced from Europe, reproduces by seed. It spreads by rooting at the lower nodes. Stems are erect or decumbent, spread from the plant's base, and are 6 inches to 2 feet long. Leaf blades are flat, 1/4 to 1/2 inch wide, to 4 inches long, and narrow. Leaf sheaths are hairy and leaf midribs have short, soft hairs on both surfaces. Three to 11 slender, finger-like spikes, each 2 to 6 inches long and arise from a short axis. Each purple to red-brown spikelet is about 1/8 inch long with a single fertile floret. Seeds are about 3/32 inch long, slender, and dark green. It is a serious pest in lawns throughout the world, becoming evident in late summer and autumn.

SMOOTH CRABGRASS, small crabgrass [*Digitaria ischaemum* (Schreb. ex Schweig.) Schreb. ex Muhl.] is similar to large crabgrass, but smaller and brighter green. Leaf sheaths are not hairy. Spikelets are about 1/12 inch long. Stems are 1/2 to 2 feet long with 1 to 4 inch long leaves. Seeds are pointed, oval, dark brown to black and 1/16 inch long.

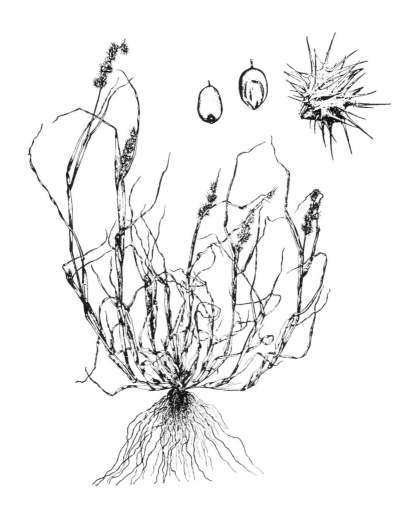

FIELD SANDBUR, burgrass [*Cenchrus incertus* M.A.Curtis]. Grass family. Panicgrass tribe. Field sandbur, a warm-season annual with tufted stems was intro-duced from Europe and reproduces by seed. Stems are 8 inches to 3 feet long but are usually prostrate and often form mats. Early stems are erect but later they are decumbent and much branched. Leaf sheaths are somewhat flattened, very loose, and smooth with hairy margins. Leaf blades are folded to flat at maturity, rough, 2 to 6 inches long, about 1/4 inch wide, dark green, and round on their margins. Spikes are 1 to 3 inches long and bear clusters of 10 to 30 burs. Each bur is about 1/4 inch in diameter and thickly set with 15 to 30 stout, sharp spines. The bur usually contains two light brown oval to oblong seeds, about 1/8 inch long. Burs cause mechanical injury to livestock and are bad in sheep wool. It grows in cultivated fields and pastures and favors sandy soil. It is widespread especially in the eastern half of Colorado from 3,500 to 6,500 feet.

WILD-PROSO MILLET, proso millet, broom-corn millet (*Panicum miliaceum* L.). Grass family. Panicgrass tribe. Wild proso millet, an annual that reproduces by seed, may have been introduced from China. The plants can be distinguished from most other weedy annual grasses at any stage of development, by the long spreading hairs on the leaf sheaths. It is similar to *P. capillare* but stems of wild-proso millet range from 2 to 6 feet tall, much larger than *P. capillare*. Leaf blades are hairy, 1/2 to 3/4 inch wide, usually 12 inches long, and rounded at the base. The ligule is a fringe of dense hairs, fused to a prominent basal membrane. Compact to more commonly spreading panicles are 6 to 12 inches wide and 4 to 18 inches long, usually nodding, and do not fully emerge from the leaf sheath. Numerous panicle branches are ascending, rough to touch, and bear spikelets toward the ends. Each 2 inch long spikelet consists of a sterile and fertile floret and each fertile floret has a caryopsis enclosed by a hard, smooth, shiny lemma and palea. There are prominent light colored nerves on the fertile lemma and palea. Shiny seeds are olive-brown to black and may darken with age. The seed coat commonly remains attached to seedling plants. Seeds are usually no more than 1/8 inch wide and only slightly longer. Some seeds normally shatter on the ground prior to harvest but they are also harvested with many crops. It is found in irrigated areas in Eastern Colorado.

WITCHGRASS, ticklegrass, panicgrass, tumbleweedgrass (*Panicum capillare* L.).
Grass family. Panicgrass-tribe. This introduced annual reproduces by seed. Stems are
stout, erect or decumbent at the base, and 1 to 2 feet tall. Leaf sheaths are very
hairy while blades are less hairy and 3 to 10 inches long. Leaf blades are 1/8 to 1/2
inch wide. The panicle is spreading, 3 to 14 inches long, breaks off at maturity and
tumbles. Spikelets are one-flowered. Seeds are narrowly oval, smooth, glossy, green
to yellow-brown and up to 1/16 inch long. It is a common weed on cultivated land
and in grain fields on sandy soil. Witchgrass is widespread in Colorado from 3,500
to 9,000 feet.

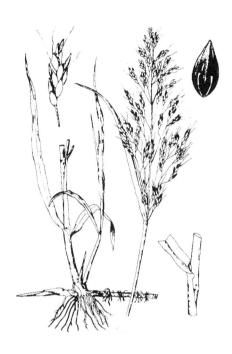

JOHNSONGRASS [*Sorghum halepense* (L.) Pers.]. Noxious. Grass family. Bluestem tribe. A creeping perennial introduced from the Mediterranean region of Europe that reproduces by seed and stout horizontal rhizomes. Erect stems are round and solid with prominent nodes and grow 2 to 8 feet tall. Johnsongrass resembles sudangrass, (*S. sudanense*). Flat leaf blades have conspicuous midveins, are up to 1 inch wide, smooth, and 12 to 18 inches long. Ligules are short membranes with a prominent fringe. There are no auricles. Flowers and seeds are borne in large, loose, open to somewhat contracted panicles. Spikelets are reddish to purple and often tipped with bent, needle-like awns. It may be poisonous to livestock due to the presence of hydrocyanic acid as a result of interruption of normal growth by drought. It is weedy in southeastern Colorado from 3,500 to 4,200 feet.

SORGHUM-ALMUM (*Sorghum almum* Parod.). Noxious. Grass family. Bluestem tribe. Sorghum almum is a johnsongrass-grain sorghum hybrid. It is a weak perennial that reproduces by seed and short thick rhizomes. It resembles johnsongrass but is taller (up to 10 feet) and coarser with fewer leaves. Inflorescences are longer, lax, and more spreading with more branches. The seed is similar to johnsongrass but in general somewhat larger but it is difficult to distinguish with certainty. It is not as strongly rhizomatous or as aggressive or persistent as johnsongrass and is inferior in quality to forage sorghums. It is chiefly a threat because of the impossibility of preventing johnsongrass seed being introduced in sorghum-almum seed and the possibility the latter will revert to johnsongrass.

43

SHATTERCANE, wild cane [*Sorghum bicolor* (L.) Moench = S. bicolor subsp. drummondii (Steud.) de Wet]. Grass family. Bluestem tribe. Shattercane, an escaped forage sorghum, has assumed weedy characteristics because of its ability to reproduce from seed that can remain viable in soil for several years. It is an annual. The erect, smooth stems can grow 12 feet tall and several stems and tillers grow from one crown supported by a fibrous root system. The plant resembles forage sorghums and sudangrass. Leaves are 12 to 24 inches long, and up to 2 to 3 inches wide. Glumes are black to brown or red-black, nerved and leathery in texture. The ligule is a fringed membrane. Seeds are borne in a loose or contracted sorghum-like panicle, 3 to 15 inches long, which often nods at maturity. Seeds resemble forage sorghum seed. It is present in eastern Colorado.

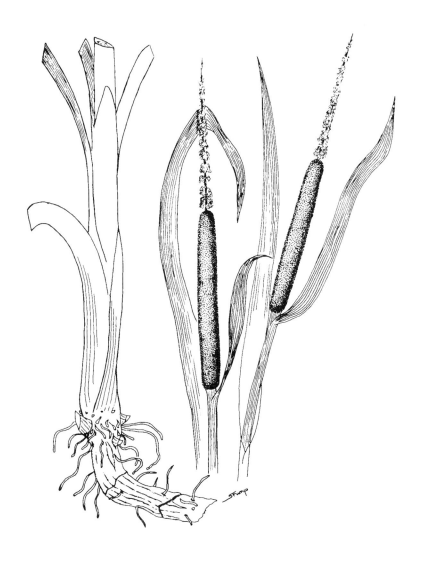

COMMON CATTAIL, Broad-leaved cattail, cattail (*Typha latifolia* L.). Cattail family.
Common cattail is a perennial plant of wet areas and grows in, unjointed, erect,
cylindrical, stout, pithy stems from 4 to 8 feet tall. It arises from large, creeping,
scaly rhizomes. The leaves are slightly taller than the spike inflorescence and are
long, linear, alternate, broad (3/8 to 7/8 inch wide), parallel veined, flat, rather
spongy, and gray-green with sheathing bases. The flowers are of two types. Pistillate
or female flowers are grouped on the stem contiguous with and below the terminal
staminate or male flowers. The staminate flowers form a 1/2 to 1 foot long, velvety-
brown, cigar-shaped spike (cattail). The cylindrical flower head eventually releases
numerous very small seeds, each enveloped in the cotton (whitish pistillate hairs) of
the cattail. The plant grows throughout Colorado from 4,000 to 7,500 feet in
marshes, shallow lakes, and irrigation ditches. This species is similar to narrow-
leaved cattail *(T. angustifolia* L.) in which the leaves grow taller than the spike but
are narrower. Pistillate and staminate flowers are separated by a short distance in
narrow-leaved cattail.

WILD ONION (*Allium canadense* L.) Lily family. Wild onion, a native perennial, reproduces by bulbs, aerial bulblets and seed, although seed production is limited. The basal bulb and leaf bases have a distinct onion odor. Leaves are fleshy, basal, sheathing and cylindrical to flat. Leafless flowering stems (scapes) are 8 to 24 inches tall. White, pink to rose colored bell-shaped flowers are borne on leafless stalks in terminal umbels that become crowded with bulblets. Consumption by cattle may cause disagreeably tainted milk.

MEADOW DEATHCAMAS, *(Zigadenus venenosus* S. Wats.). Lily family. This native perennial, hairless herb has mostly basal, grasslike leaves and an underground onion-like, scaly, fibrous bulb with a dark outer covering. Sparingly leafy stems are up to 2 feet tall, unbranched and produced at flowering. The plants are 8 to 14 inches tall with sheathing, linear leaves surrounding the stem. Leaves are up to 12 inches long, flat to folded, V-creased parallel veined, and never hollow. Leaf margins are smooth to slightly rough. The open inflorescence is a dense raceme of cream to white bell-shaped flowers. Wrinkled, rough, light brown seeds are produced in a capsule. The entire plant is poisonous because it contains an alkaloid, zygacine, which is toxic to all animals, but especially to cattle and sheep. It is found in the western two-thirds of Colorado from 4,500 to 8,000 feet.

FOOTHILL DEATHCAMAS [*Zigadenus paniculatus* (Nutt.) S.Wats.] differs because the panicle is a compact, terminal plume rather than being open and branched as it is in meadow death camas.

CALIFORNIA FALSEHELLEBORE, skunk cabbage, corn lily (*Veratrum californicum* Durand). Lily family. This native, perennial, coarse, erect herb, grows 3 to 6 feet tall. The unbranched leafy stems are 3 to 7 feet tall and arise from a short, thick rootstock. Sheathing leaves are alternate in three ranks and broadly oval, with prominent parallel veins. Each leaf is 6 to 12 inches long and 3 to 6 inches wide. The numerous, inconspicuous flowers are 6-parted, white, yellow-white, or green tinged on the 1 to 2 foot long raceme. It grows in low moist habitats in open woods and pastures from 8,500 to 11,000 feet. It is poisonous to humans and animals and causes "monkey face" in newborn lambs and abortion in sheep who graze it.

ROCKY MOUNTAIN IRIS, wild iris, blue flag *(Iris missouriensis* Nutt.). Iris family. A native, perennial that reproduces by seed and spreading from short, thick, rootstocks. It is similar to cultivated iris, but smaller. Nearly leafless stems are slender, erect and 1 to 2 feet tall. Basal leaves are light green, narrow, and up to 18 inches long. One to 4 attractive light blue to violet or variegated, 2 to 3 inch long flowers are borne on each stem. The fruit is an oblong capsule, 1 to 2 inches long, and bears numerous seeds. Seeds are irregularly fig-shaped, round on one side, and dished on two or three sides. The rough-wrinkled surface is light to dark red-brown and the seeds are about 3/16 inch long and half as wide. It invades moist mountain meadows where it may take over large areas in western Colorado and the San Luis Valley from 5,000 to 10,000 feet.

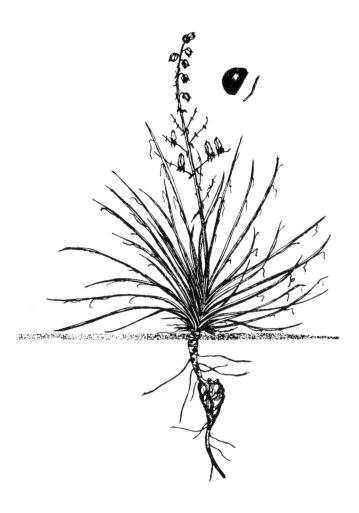

GREAT PLAINS YUCCA, soapweed, Spanish bayonet *(Yucca glauca* Nutt. Ex Fraser). Agave family. This native perennial reproduces by seeds and grows as a bunch plant with a woody base from which numerous, somewhat crowded, erect, spreading, narrow, rigid, sharp-pointed, bayonet-like leaves arise. Flat to inrolled leaves have sparingly threaded margins and are 1/4 to 1/2 inch wide and 1 to 3 feet long. Large, green to creamy-white (may be purple tinged) flowers are globose to bell-shaped, drooping, 1 1/2 to 3 inches across and are borne on open, elongated, spikelike terminal racemes on a 1 to 4 foot high central stalk. Yucca fruit is a large oblong, upright, dry capsule 1 inch or more wide and 2 to 3 inches long. It splits longitudinally into three, two-celled, seed-bearing sections. The numerous seeds are semi-round, flat, wafer-thin, winged, black, and 1/2 inch in diameter. It grows on dry plains and slopes in competition with desired grasses and is scattered over Colorado from 4,000 to 9,000 feet.

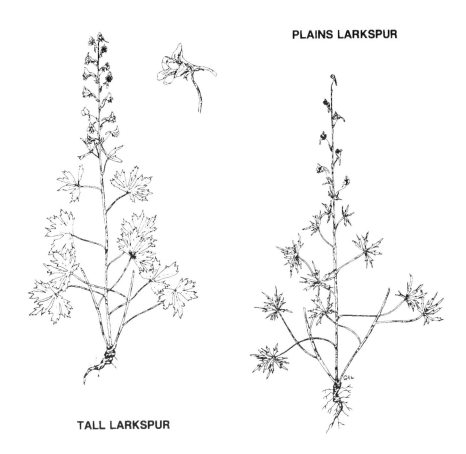

PLAINS LARKSPUR

TALL LARKSPUR

GEYER LARKSPUR, plains larkspur *(Delphinium geyeri* Greene). Crowfoot family. Larkspur, a native perennial, has a woody tuberous root that produces an erect, up to 2 foot tall, slightly hairy, hollow stem. Leaves are simple, alternate or clustered at the ground, petioled, and palmately lobed into three to five primary divisions that are again lobed and repeatedly divided into linear segments. Showy flowers occur in a terminal raceme, 1/2 to 2 feet tall, with five, predominantly purple, sepals. The upper sepal is prolonged backwards into a distinct spur. Individual seed pods are upright containing many dark seeds when ripe. When green, the entire plant is poisonous to cattle. Seeds are also toxic.

TALL LARKSPUR *(Delphinium barbeyi* (L.) Huth) is distinguished from plains larkspur because it (a) typically grows in higher mountain open moist areas, (b) is 2 to 5 feet tall, (c) is distinctly stemmed throughout most of the season, (d) flowers in the summer rather than spring, and (e) does not die back until fall. Tall larkspur is also toxic but is a less serious problem because it is less available to grazing cattle.

LOW LARKSPUR *(Delphinium nuttallianum Pritz.* ex Walp.). Leaves are distinctly parted in to narrow finger-like lobes. The plant grows only 10 to 20 inches tall. Large white, pale-blue, blue, to blue-purple flowers have prominent spurs. Three spreading, beaked seed follicles arise from each flower.

ANNUAL PRICKLEPOPPY [*Argemone polyanthemos* (Fedde) G.B.Ownbey]. Poppy family. This native annual, winter annual, or biennial grows from a deep taproot and reproduces by seed. The single stout stem is erect, rarely branched, sparingly prickly with yellow spines, 1 to 3 feet high, and contains yellow to orange-colored sap. Blue-green to gray-green leaves are alternate, smooth, clasping, irregularly and frequently deeply cleft or lobed, with spiny margins and midrib. The few flowers are terminal, large, white, 2 to 3 1/2 inches across, and petals fall soon after blooming. Yellow stamens at flower centers dry brown. The fruit is an oblong, many seeded capsule or pod, 1 to 1 1/2 inches long with stout, yellow spines. Dark brown, shiny seed is globular with a rough netted surface and a winglike ridge on one side and is 1/16 inch or more in diameter. It is a prairie plant frequently found in pastures and on roadsides scattered over Colorado from 3,500 to 7,000 feet but most common in the northeast.

STINGING NETTLE (*Urtica dioica* L.), Nettle family. Stinging nettle is a native, perennial that reproduces by seed and rhizomes and often forms dense patches. Stems are square, erect, 2 to 9 feet tall. Leaves are opposite, narrow, ovate, and have saw-toothed margins and have numerous stinging hairs over much of their surfaces. Often they are purple tinged on the underside. Plants can be monecious or dioecious. Flower clusters branch and spread and usually are larger than the subtending petiole. Flower clusters are unisexual or, if plants are dioecious, staminate or pistillate with pistillate clusters above the staminate when both are present. The numerous seeds are very small and flattened. Stems and leaves are sparsely covered with hairs containing formic acid that causes pain and inflammation on contact with skin. It is generally found along ditches, fence rows, and on roadsides. It occurs throughout Colorado but is more prevalent on the western slope from 4,500 to 9,500 feet.

GAMBEL OAK, Gambel's oak, *(Quercus gambelii* Nutt.). Oak family. Oaks are common in the U.S. varying from low shrubs to magnificent trees. Gambel oak is a perennial, hardwood shrub or small tree with gray bark. It grows from 9 to 15 or more feet tall. Leaves are broadly oval in outline, hairless, bright, shiny green above with a slightly paler lower surface. They are 2 to 4 inches long and irregularly 5 to 9 lobed, usually over half-way to the midrib. Middle lateral lobes are the largest. Alternate leaves can be pubescent on the lower surface. Young twigs are light brown and lightly pubescent. Acorns are usually 1/2 to 3/4 inch long. The cup is hemispheric to top-shaped, 3/8 to 5/8 inch wide and covers one-third to one-half of the acorn. Plants are monoecious with staminate flowers occurring in drooping clusters with 6 to 12 stamens. Pistillate flowers are inconspicuous and solitary in axils of new leaves or on small spikes and bloom in May to June. The ovary is usually three-celled but only rarely does more than one ovule mature in each pistil. The species is variable occurring most commonly from 4,000 to 8,500 feet in southcentral and southwestern Colorado. It can be poisonous to cattle and occasionally sheep and goats. The most dangerous period is early spring during sprouting of new foliage. As leaves mature toxicity decreases.

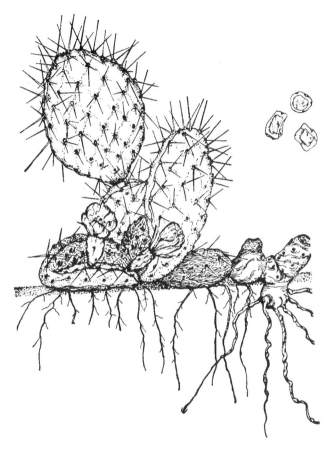

PLAINS PRICKLYPEAR, cactus, opuntia, pricklypear (*Opuntia polycantha* Haw.).
Cactus family. A perennial that reproduces by seed and by rooting at stem joints. Flat
stems are normally prostrate but may be up to 3 feet tall, thick, succulent, rounded to
oval joints each 2 to 6 inches long and 2 to 4 inches wide, or larger. Each stem (the
cactus pad) is covered with sharp, stiff, 1/2 to about 1 inch long white to yellow
spines that may be surrounded by smaller bristles. Small, scaly leaves on young
branches drop early. Stem joints root freely at the margins to form extensive clumps
or, if broken off, may give rise to new plants. Roots are fibrous. Large flowers are
bright yellow, orange, or red, 2 to 4 inches across, sometimes with red centers.
There are 8 to 12 petals and many stamens. The fruit is up to 2 inches long, pear-
shaped, smooth, fleshy, and edible but they may be dry and spiny. Seeds are oval to
round, flattened, white to straw-colored and about 3/16 inch in diameter. It is found
on rangeland and its population increases with overgrazing and in dry seasons as a
result of reduced grass competition. It may serve as an emergency feed for livestock if
spines are burned off, but an excessive amount may be injurious. There are numerous
species in the west and several are found in Colorado from 4,000 to 7,500 feet.

GREASEWOOD [*Sarcobatus vermiculatus* (Hook.) Torr.]. Goosefoot family. This native, perennial shrub has spiny, much branched, rigid stems. Young stems are yellow and with age, become gray or whitish because of fine hairs. Many branches are tipped with a spine. It grows from 1 to 9 feet ttll. Linear leaves are deciduous, 1/4 to 1 inch long, fleshy, round in cross section, alternate, bright green and attached directly to the stem. They are opposite below and alternate above. Yellow flowers appear in late-summer. It is monecious, with female flowers axillary and inconspicuous and male flowers crowded above in terminal spikes, each about 3/4 inch long. Greasewood contains a soluble oxalate poison; cattle are rarely poisoned on rangeland, but sheep are more susceptible. It is usually confined to alkaline soils throughout western Colorado from 4,500 to 8,500 feet.

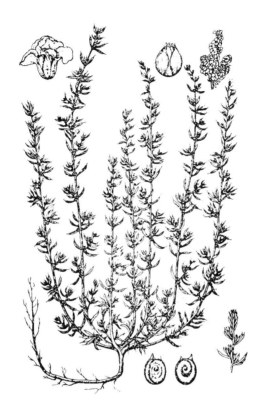

HALOGETON *[Halogeton glomeratus* (Stephen ex Bieb.) C.A.Mey.]. Noxious.
Goosefoot family. Halogeton is an introduced annual that reproduces by seed. Its
stems are smooth, branch from the base, and then grow erect to form a round, bushy
plant. Plants are blue-green in spring and early summer and become red or reddish-
yellow by late summer. Stems are usually red to purple tinged and grow a few to 18
inches tall, depending on conditions. Large plants can be 3 feet in diameter. Leaves
are fleshy, tubular or wiener-shaped, and 1/4 to 1/2 inch long. The blunt end is
tipped with a delicate, needle-like spine. Flowers are yellow or green, of two kinds,
and mostly inconspicuous in leaf axils. Seeds are also of two kinds, and conspicuously winged and frequently so crowded on the stems as to constitute the only visible
portion. The spiral embryo is indicative of halogeton's close relationship to Russian
thistle. Large plants may break off and blow as tumbleweeds. It is a prolific seed
producer through most of the summer. The original infestation was reported from
Nevada in 1934. The first Colorado infestation was along railroad spurs near the
Utah line where sheep from an infested area were unloaded. It contains an oxalate
poisonous to sheep and has caused heavy losses when other forage was limited. It
grows on saline and desert land, but is also an aggressive invader of other grazing
areas.

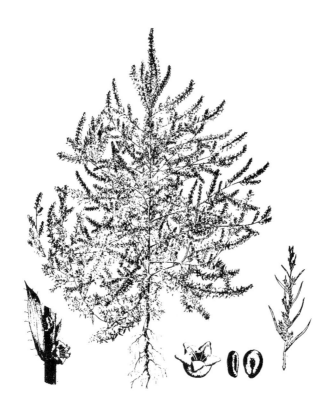

KOCHIA, fireweed, Mexican fireweed [*Kochia scoparia* (L.) Schrad.]. Goosefoot family. This native of Asia introduced from Europe is an annual that reproduces by seed. Stems are erect, round, slender, pale green, much branched, usually soft-hairy but often smooth, red-tinged, and 1 to 6 feet tall. Alternate leaves have 3 or 5 prominent veins, are 1/2 to 2 inches long, lance-shaped or linear and hairy, especially on the margins. Upper leaf surfaces are smooth and the lower is hairy. Upper leaves are narrow. Flowers are inconspicuous, sessile in the axils of the upper leaves, and form short, dense, bracted spikes. Seeds are about 1/16 inch long, wedge-shaped, dull brown and slightly ribbed. In autumn the plants may become reddish and later brown. It grows in cultivated fields up to 8,500 feet.

FIVEHOOK BASSIA, hyssop bassia [*Bassia hyssopifolia* (Pallas) Ktze.] Goosefoot family. Bassia was introduced from the Caspian Sea region of Europe. It is an annual that reproduces by seeds and resembles kochia, but is not as prevalent. Flowers and fruit are in axils of the upper bractlike leaves, and form elongated, slender, woolly spikes. Seeds are small, flattened, brown, and are either encased in a thin covering or remain in the woolly calyx that has a curved hook on each of five segments, which is the characteristic that distinguishes it from kochia. It grows well in alkaline soil and is scattered over Colorado from 4,000 to 7,000 feet.

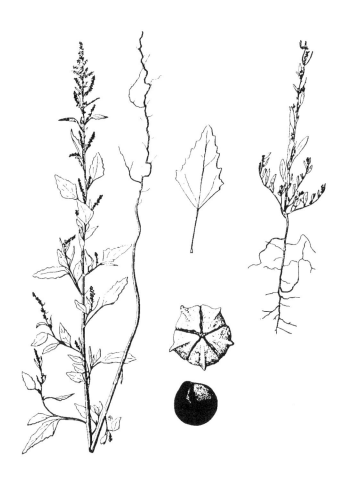

COMMON LAMBSQUARTERS, white goosefoot, lambsquarters *(Chenopodium album* L.). Goosefoot family. A common annual introduced from Europe. It is a native of Asia and reproduces by seed. Stems are solitary, erect, 1 to 6 feet tall, stout, smooth, grooved, often striped with pink or purple with ascending branches. Leaves are alternate, commonly 1 1/2 times as long as wide, with lower ones ovate or goosefoot-shaped and upper ones becoming narrower. They are commonly all white-mealy underneath but are sometimes green on both sides. Inflorescences are small compact clusters, green, clustered into dense paniculate spikes. Flowers are crowded in axils and at tips of stems and branches. Five, white, mealy sepals are not or only modestly keeled and enclose fruit at maturity. Seed is 1/16 inch in diameter, lens-shaped, shiny black, smooth, and may remain dormant in soil for years. It is a succulent, fast-growing plant that rapidly removes moisture from soil. It grows in cultivated fields and gardens throughout Colorado and the United States.

NETSEED LAMBSQUARTERS *(Chenopodium berlandieri* Moq.). Similar to above except that seed is minutely roughened rather than smooth. May be even more common in Colorado than common lambsquarters. NOTE - This genus is extremely variable and seedlings are nearly impossible to distinguish. Common lambsquarters is one of the most abundant of broadleaved species but its presumed abundance may be based on improper identification and incorrect inclusion of other species as common lambsquarters.

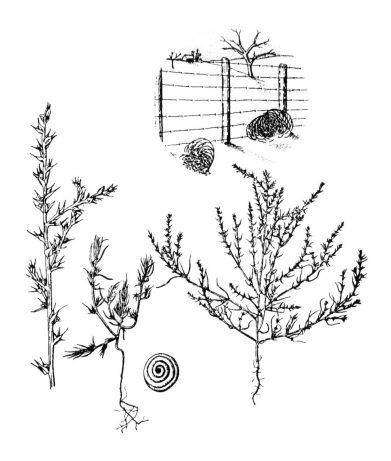

RUSSIAN THISTLE, Russian tumbleweed, tumbling thistle *(Salsola iberica* Sennen & Pau). Goosefoot family. Russian thistle, introduced to South Dakota in flaxseed from Russia about 1873, is an annual that reproduces by seed. It is a round, bushy, much-branched plant growing 1 to 3 feet tall. Stems are usually red or purple striped. Branches are slender, succulent when young and woody when mature. Leaves are alternate with the first ones long, dark green, soft, slender, and 1 to 2 1/2 inches long. Later leaves are-short, stiff, tipped with a spine, and not over 1/2 inch long, with two sharp-pointed bracts at the base. Flowers are small, inconspicuous, green-white or pink, usually solitary in leaf axils, and accompanied by a pair of spiny bracts. Seeds are about 1/16 inch in diameter and conical with each enclosed in a calyx with a papery margin. At maturity, plants break off at the base and because they are round they become tumbleweeds, scattering seeds for long distances. Young, green succulent plants are used for forage when other food is scarce. It grows in dry areas and cultivated fields, principally in grain-growing areas. It is widespread over Colorado up to 8,500 feet.

PROSTRATE PIGWEED, matted pigweed, spreading amaranth (*Amaranthus blitoides* S.Wats = *A. graecizans* auctt., non L.). Amaranth family. A tap-rooted annual, native to the eastern states and introduced west of the Mississippi probably from S.America. The smooth, pale green plant with a much branched, prostrate stem that spreads in all directions on the ground to form a mat reproduces by seed. Pliable stems are fleshy, nearly smooth, usually red to purple tinged, and 12 to 18 inches long. Leaves are alternate, small, oval to egg-shaped, broadest at the tip, and narrow into slender petioles each 1/4 to 3/4 inch long, and bristle-tipped. Flowers are small, green with short bracts and occur in small, congested clusters in leaf axils. The fruit is almost round, dry and has a smooth sack enclosing the seed. Seeds are numerous, round, lens-shaped, shiny, jet-black, and about 1/16 inch in diameter. It grows in cultivated fields in much of the United States and in Colorado up to 8,500 feet.

REDROOT PIGWEED, rough pigweed, redroot (*Amaranthus retroflexus* L.). Amaranth family. Redroot pigweed, an annual that reproduces by seed, was introduced from Europe or tropical America. The stem is light green, erect, stout, tough, rough-hairy, much branched and 1 to 6 feet (usually 2 to 3) tall, commonly red-striped below, with a long, somewhat fleshy, red taproot. Leaves are long-petioled, alternate with the lower ones ovate, about 3 to 6 inches long, pointed at the tip, dull green, rough-hairy (especially on lower surface along veins), with prominent ribs and veins. Upper leaves are smaller, narrower and more lance-shaped. Flowers are small, green and densely crowded in large, bristly, irregular, simple or branched, terminal or axillary clusters. Flower clusters have many stiff, spine-like scales. The numerous seeds are small, oval, lens-shaped, about 1/25 inch long, jet-black, shiny and remain viable for many years. It grows throughout the United States and in Colorado up to 8,500 feet.

SMOOTH PIGWEED, slender pigweed, green pigweed, (*Amaranthus hybridus* L.). This weed is very similar to *A. retroflexus* in its gross morphology. The primary distinguishing characteristic is in *A. hybridus* outer sepals are acute and in *A. retroflexus* they are rounded. The two species intermingle and are difficult to distinguish. There is no evidence of differences in susceptibility to control.

COMMON WATERHEMP, waterhemp, *(Amaranthus rudis* Sauer). A dioecious annual herb with a strong taproot. Stems are stout, erect or ascending from 1.5 to 6 feet tall, simple or with a few ascending branches. Leaves are alternate with oblong to lance-oblong blades, 1 to 4 inches long and rounded at apex. Upper leaves are much reduced and narrowly oblong with up to 2 inch petioles. Spikelike inflorescence has axillary clusters of flowers with short bracts in which the midrib extends beyond the bract margin. Male flowers have five sepals, female flowers only 1 or 2. Seed is round, lens shaped, reddish-brown to black, smooth and shiny. This species easily hybridizes with other Amaranthaceae and intermediate forms are common. It is found in fields and commonly along stream banks and in floodplains.

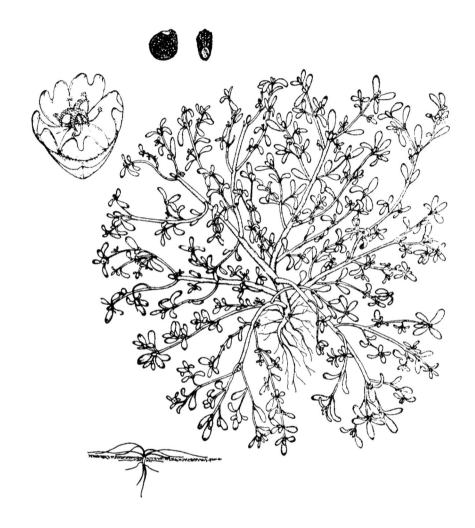

COMMON PURSLANE, purslane (*Portulaca oleracea* L.). Purslane family. This prostrate annual, introduced from Europe, reproduces by seed. Purplish-red stems are 2 to 12 inches long, fleshy, round, smooth and freely branching from a deep central root to form a dense mat. Succulent, smooth leaves are alternate, obovate, or wedge-shaped with rounded tips, small, smooth, fleshy, 1/4 to 1 1/2 inches long, and primarily clustered at the ends of the branches. Flowers are yellow, 5-petalled, about 1/4 inch broad, and are borne singly in leaf axils. They open only in brightest sunshine. Many very small black seeds less than 1/32 inch in diameter are produced. It readily takes root after being cut off and the fleshy leaves dry slowly. It grows throughout most of the United States and in Colorado up to 8,500 feet.

BOUNCINGBET, soapwort, sweet-betty *(Saponaria officinalis* L.). Pink family. An introduced creeping perennial from Europe reproducing by seed and rhizomes. The sparingly branched stems are erect, smooth, stout, 1 to 3 feet tall and have swollen nodes. Leaves usually occur in 10 to 20 pairs with the lower ones withering and deciduous by flowering. They are opposite, ovate or oval, pointed, three-nerved from the base, are smooth, rather thick and 2 to 4 inches long. The showy pink or white flowers are fragrant, about 1 inch across and in dense terminal clusters at the end of the main stem and branches. Petals are white to pink and usually notched at the apex. The tubular but not inflated, thin, pliable 20-nerved calyx is green and sometimes purple-tinged. It narrows to 5 triangular, deeply cleft teeth. The fruit is an oblong toothed capsule. Seeds are dull black, rough, kidney-shaped, and no more than 1/12 inch across. It is an escaped ornamental whose roots were once used as a substitute for soap. It grows in yards, pastures, along ditch banks, and roadways but is seldom found in cultivated fields. It is common in the eastern United States and is found in northern Colorado up to 7,500 feet.

COMMON CHICKWEED [*Stellaria media* (L.) Vill.]. Pink family. This introduced annual or winter annual reproduces by seeds and creeping stems that can root at nodes. Stems are slender, 4 to 16 inches long, much branched, creeping, rooting at the nodes or ascending, with a conspicuous line of hairs on one side, and form mats. Leaves are opposite, oval, usually acute, up to 1 1/2 inches long. Upper leaves lack petioles, lower have petioles and are hairy toward the base. Flowers are white, starshaped, about 1/4 inch broad, and are borne solitary in leaf axils or in terminal clusters. Petals are deeply two-parted. Seeds are small, about 1/32 inch across, round, rough, brown, and numerous in a dry capsule. Seed remains viable for many years in soil. Common chickweed grows in fields, nurseries, and gardens but is especially troublesome in lawns, and does well in shady areas. It is found mostly in central and north-central Colorado from 5,000 to 10,000 feet.

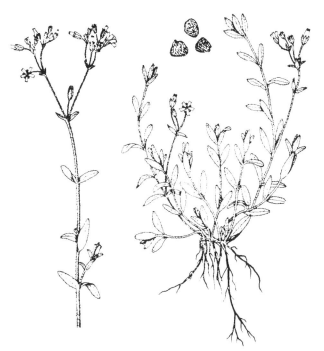

MOUSEEAR CHICKWEED, common chickweed *(Cerastium vulgatum* L.). Pink family. This creeping perennial was introduced from Europe. It reproduces by seed and creeping stems that root at nodes. Stems are tufted with some prostrate, 4 to 28 inches long, and others ascending. They are bright green, with sticky hairs throughout. Opposite leaves are sessile, small, oblong, entire, pointed, and 1/3 to 1 inch long. Flowers are small, white and borne in loose terminal clusters. The fruit is a small cylindrical capsule or pod about 1/3 inch long containing many tiny (about 1/40 inch across) tuberculate, brown seeds. It grows in fields, lawns, and gardens but is especially troublesome in lawns that are excessively shaded or watered. It is distributed throughout the United States and in north-central, central, and south-central Colorado from 3,500 to 10,000 feet.

FIELD CHICKWEED *(Cerastium arvense* L.). Pink family. In contrast to *C. vulgatum* this is a native, clumped to mat-forming perennial. It reproduces by seed and short, creeping stems that root at nodes. The stems are slender and may or may not root at nodes. They ascend and grow 4 to 12 inches long and frequently form mats. It is similar to mouseear chickweed, but the leaves are narrow, 1 to 1 1/2 inches long. Flowers are about 1/2 inch broad. The capsule is about 3/8 inch long. Seed is larger, 1/32 inch across, somewhat smoother and rounder than those of *C. vulgatum.* It is found in the western two-thirds of Colorado from 5,000 to 12,500 feet.

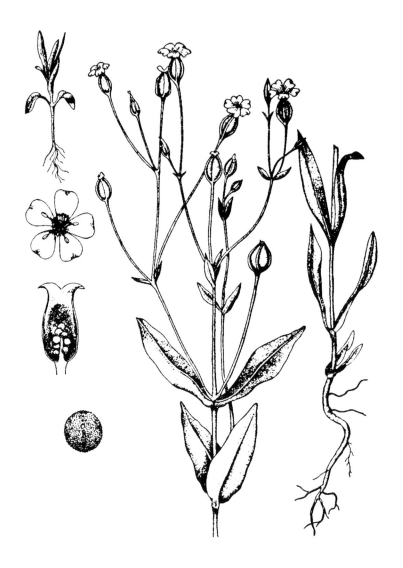

COWCOCKLE, pink cockle, cowherb, *(Vaccaria pyrimidata* Medicus). Pink family. An introduced, tap-rooted annual from Europe that reproduces by seed. The gray-green stem is erect, slender, round, 1 1/2 to 3 feet tall, smooth, swollen at the nodes, and branched above. Leaves are lance-shaped or long ovate, pointed at the apex and clasping the stem at the base, smooth, and opposite. Lower leaves may have short petioles or are sessile. Inconspicuous flowers grow in loose open clusters. They are deep pink or red, 1/4 to 3/4 inch across and have five toothed petals. The smooth, inflated calyx is about 1/2 inch long and strongly five-ribbed with green or purplish veins. Fruit remains in the calyx at maturity. Seeds are 1/10 inch in diameter, round, black to gray, and remain viable for several years. Seeds are poison-ous and undesirable in wheat that is to be used for flour. It is widely distributed in the United States and in Colorado up to 7,500 feet.

PALE DOCK

CURLY DOCK

BROADLEAF DOCK

CURLY DOCK, yellow dock, narrow-leaved dock, sour dock *(Rumex crispus* L.) Noxious. Buckwheat family. Curly dock was introduced from Europe and is a perennial that grows from a long taproot. It reproduces by seed and by shoots from the crown. It grows erect with slender, reddish, ridged stems, each 2 to 5 feet tall, unbranched or with a few branches at the top. As is common in the buckwheat family, each stem node is sheathed with a papery stipule. Leaves are mostly basal, alternate, 4 to 12 inches long, crisp, with wavy margins and no hairs. Basal leaves have long petioles. The large, terminal inflorescence with ascending branches can be up to 12 inches long. Small, green flowers are borne in long cylindrical clusters. The winged fruit holds an achene that is three-cornered, red-brown, and 1/12 inch long. It is common in pastures and grows vigorously on moist soil. It is a bad weed in alfalfa grown for seed. It is found throughout the United States and Canada and throughout Colorado from 3,500 to 8,500 feet.

BROADLEAF DOCK, bitter dock, blunt-leaved dock (*Rumex obtusifolius* L.). Buckwheat family. This perennial weed, introduced from Europe is a native of Asia and reproduces by seed. The plant is smooth, dark green with a stout, erect, grooved, simple or sparingly branched, 1 to 3 1 1/2 feet high stem. Alternate leaves are broader than those of curly dock, alternate, and the lower ones are 4 to 12 inches long, half as broad, and heart-shaped, with rounded or bluntly pointed tips. Leaf veins are somewhat hairy underneath. Upper leaves are narrower and more pointed. Flowers are borne on slender pedicels in separated loose whorls or clusters, on ascending branches and form an open panicle. The achene is dark red, shiny, three-cornered and 1/12 inch long. Each achene has 1 to 3 spines on its wing structure that distinguish them from those of curly dock. It grows in fields and meadows throughout the United States and in northeastern and north-central Colorado from 3,500 to 5,100 feet.

PALE DOCK (*Rumex altissimus* Wood). Buckwheat family. Pale dock is a native perennial that grows from a large taproot. Stems are erect, 3 or more feet tall, ribbed, branched below the inflorescence, with one or several from the crown. Basal leaves are 6 to 12 inches long petioled, narrow to broad lance-shaped, flat with smooth margins, and form a rosette. Stem leaves are smaller, alternate, with papery sheaths at the base of short stalks surrounding the stem. Imperfect flowers are small, green early and red-brown at maturity, and occur in compact clusters on numerous terminal branches. Achenes are sharply three-angled, shiny, brown and about 1/8 inch long. It grows in pastures, meadows, and along ditches and roadsides. It is found mostly in the western two-thirds of Colorado from 4,500 to 10,000 feet.

VEINY DOCK, winged dock, wild begonia, wild hydrangea (*Rumex venosus* Pursh).
Buckwheat family. A creeping perennial introduced from Europe, that reproduces by
seed and wide-spreading rhizomes. The stem is stout, erect, and 6 to 15 inches high.
Leaves are oval to oblong, 1 to 4 inches long and leathery and lower leaves are
reduced. Flowering stems are erect, red-tinged and often branched. Flowers not
crowded and inconspicuous. In fruit, the plant is characterized by large, erect,
showy, red fruiting clusters. Their color is due to the numerous red calyxes with
conspicuous wings, each 1/2 to 1 1/4 inches broad, veiny, with a deep cleft at their
base. The achene is about 1/4 inch long, smooth and shiny with concave faces.
Veiny dock grows along railroad embankments and on roadsides. Although it is a
creeping perennial that does not withstand cultivation. It is found in the eastern half
of Colorado and in the northwest from 3,500 to 8,500 feet.

RED SORREL, sheep sorrel, field sorrel (*Rumex acetosella* L.). Buckwheat family. This weed was introduced from Europe. It is a creeping perennial that reproduces by seeds and slender creeping rhizomes. Stems are erect, smooth, red, slender, 4 to 24 inches high, and simple or branched and somewhat woody at the base. Basal leaves are alternate, narrow, arrowhead shaped, 1 to 6 inches long, smooth, light green, with spreading basal lobes. Upper leaves are more slender and often lack conspicuous basal lobes. Slender leaf petioles have a papery stipule at the stem junction. Plants are dioecious or polygamous. Flowers occur in erect, 2 to 6 inch long, terminal racemes, staminate flowers are orange-yellow and pistillate flowers are red-orange. The achene is red-brown, three-cornered, and only 1/25 inch long. It may be poisonous to sheep. It grows in lawns, meadows, and pastures in most parts of the United States. It is found in north-central, central, and south-central Colorado from 4,500 to 10,000 feet.

PENNSYLVANIA SMARTWEED

LADYSTHUMB

PENNSYLVANIA SMARTWEED, Pennsylvania knotweed (*Polygonum pensylvanicum* L.). Buckwheat family. Pennsylvania smartweed, a native annual, reproduces by seed. Its stem is erect or spreading, much branched and grows 1 to 3 feet long. Stems may root at lower nodes. Each swollen stem node is surrounded by a tubular, papery stipule. Leaves are alternate, lance-shaped, 2 to 8 inches long, with both ends pointed and lower leaves are borne on short petioles. Flowers are rose or pink and occur in erect, short, crowded, cylindrical or oblong, usually blunt spikes each of which is 1 to 2 inches long. Achenes are small, lens-shaped sometimes three-angled, about 1/8 inch long and black, smooth, and shiny. It grows in moist soil in fields, pastures, and meadows in many parts of the United States. It is found mostly in the eastern half of Colorado up to 5,500 feet.

LADYSTHUMB *(Polygonum persicaria* L.). Buckwheat family. An introduced annual that reproduces by seed. It is similar to Pennsylvania smartweed but smaller. Stems are 8 to 30 inches high and short-petioled leaves are 1 to 7 inches long, usually with a triangular dark spot near the center. Leaf sheath margins are distinctly bristly-hairy. The achene is 1/10 inch long. It is scattered in cultivated areas in Colorado from 3,500 to 7,500 feet.

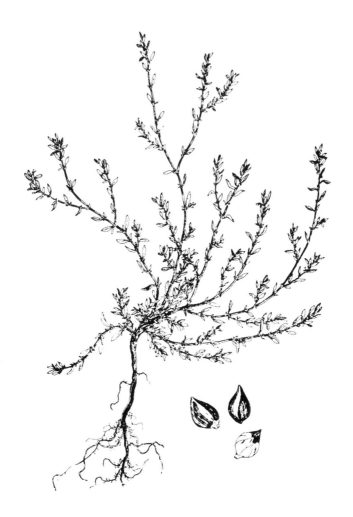

PROSTRATE KNOTWEED, doorweed, matweed *(Polygonum aviculare* L.). Buckwheat family. An introduced, mat-forming annual that grows from a taproot and reproduces by seed. The stem is pale green, slender, usually prostrate but sometimes ultimate branches ascend. Stems grow 4 inches to 3 feet long in all directions from the root and are much branched. Each node is sheathed by the remnant of a papery stipule. Leaves are alternate, blue-green (gray-green when infected with mildew fungi), small, lance-shaped or oblong, usually somewhat pointed and 1/4 to 1 inch long. Upper leaves are normally 1/2 the size of lower leaves. Inflorescences are small, inconspicuous, and grow solitary or in clusters of 3 to 6 flowers in leaf axils. The five petals and sepals are green with white or pink margins. The achene is dull brown, three-cornered, and up to 1/10 inch long. This is a very tough, durable plant and is more of a problem in gardens, lawns, and yards than in cultivated fields. It is widely distributed over Colorado up to 9,500 feet.

ERECT KNOTWEED *(Polygonum erectum* L.). Is similar to prostrate knotweed but grows up to 20 inches tall and spreads somewhat. Infloresences are 2 to 3 flowered on short axilary branches.

WILD BUCKWHEAT, climbing buckwheat, black bindweed (*Polygonum convolvulus* L.). Buckwheat family. This weed, introduced from Europe, is a native of Asia. It is an annual that reproduces by seed. The stem is slightly angular, smooth or somewhat scaly, slender, branching, trailing or twining, and grows up to 3 feet long. Nodes are sheathed by an inconspicuous papery stipule. Alternate leaves are 1/2 to 3 inches long, arrow- or heart-shaped, pointed, smooth, dark green, with somewhat hairy margins, and are borne on slender petioles. Seedlings have distinctly heart-shaped leaves. Petioles of lower leaves about equal the blade and upper leaves are gradually reduced. Clusters of small green-white flowers grow in axillary clusters or in slender, loosely flowered, terminal racemes. The achene is dull black, pointed, three-cornered, and about 1/8 inch long. The plant resembles field bindweed or wild morning-glory in the shape of its leaves and its twining habits. It can always be-distinguished by its small flower and single taproot. It grows in cultivated fields throughout the United States. It is widespread in Colorado up to 9,000 feet but most prevalent on irrigated acreage.

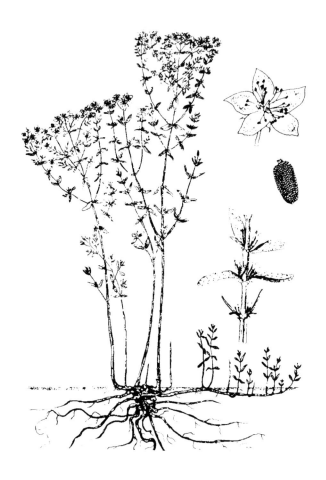

COMMON ST. JOHNSWORT, klamathweed, St. Johnswort (*Hypericum perforatum* L.). Noxious. St. Johnswort family. An introduced, erect, creeping perennial that reproduces by seed and rhizomes. Short horizontal roots may be 1/2 to 3 inches deep. Occasional procumbent stems may send up weak shoots, but apparently do not develop roots. Rust-colored stems are erect from a woody base, much branched, 1 to 3 feet tall. Young stems are somewhat two-edged. Leaves are numerous, sessile, entire, opposite, 1/8 inch wide, 1/2 to 1 inch long, with translucent dots over the surface. Bright yellow flowers have five separate petals with infrequent, small black dots along their margins and occur in showy terminal clusters. Yellow stamens are numerous and arranged in three clusters. The fruit is a pod containing numerous, very small, cylindrical, finely-pitted, dark brown seeds, each about 1/24 inch long. It is somewhat poisonous to livestock, but is most serious as an aggressive invader of grazing land, frequently as a result of overgrazing. Known infestations in Colorado include a large north-central area and a few small infestations on the Western Slope.

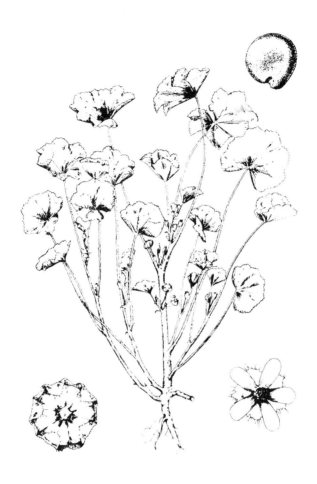

COMMON MALLOW, roundleaf mallow, cheeseweed (*Malva neglecta* Wallr.). Mallow family. An introduction from Europe. It is an annual, winter annual, or biennial that reproduces by seed. Stems are round, smooth, prostrate, somewhat pubescent, usually branched from base, 6 inches to 3 feet long and spread over the ground in all directions from a deep taproot. Alternate leaves are round or kidney-shaped, 1 to 3 inches across, slightly lobed with scalloped and toothed edges, and are borne on slender petioles each 3 to 6 inches long. The 1/3 to 1/2 inch broad flowers are clustered in leaf axils and are pale blue to white and sometimes pink. The fruit is composed of about 15 kidney-shaped carpels arranged in a circle, resembling a large wheel of cheese. It is mucilaginous and sweet tasting when green. Each segment contains one flattened, round, deeply notched, smooth, red-brown seed, 1/16 to 1/12 inch in diameter. It grows in cultivated ground, gardens, and lawns throughout the United States and Canada and over Colorado except in the extreme east from 4,500 to 7,000 feet.

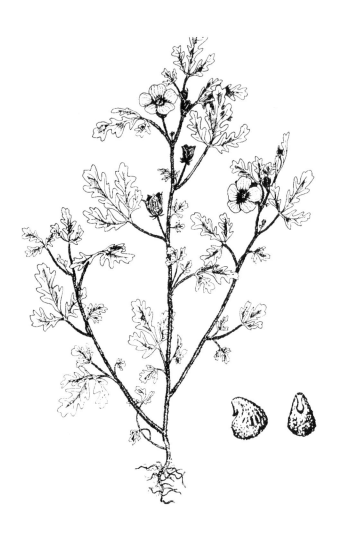

VENICE MALLOW, flower-of-an-hour, *(Hibiscus trionum* L.). Mallow family. An introduced annual from southern Europe that reproduces by seed. It is a hairy, low-growing plant, branching from the base and 1/2 to 11/2 feet tall. Stems widely branched from a central base and tend to be spreading rather than erect. Leaves are alternate, deeply divided into 3 or 5 toothed lobes, with a petiole about as long as the blade. One to 2 inch diameter flowers have white to pale yellow petals with a purple or black center. One edge and the base of each petal is dark purple. Each flower remains open only a short time and petals fall quickly. The fruit with numerous seeds is enclosed in a hairy, membranous, bladderlike calyx with prominent nerves, subtended by narrow bracts. Seeds are triangular to kidney-shaped, with a pimpled surface, gray-brown to black and about 1/12 inch long. It is scattered over Colorado from 4,000 to 5,500 feet.

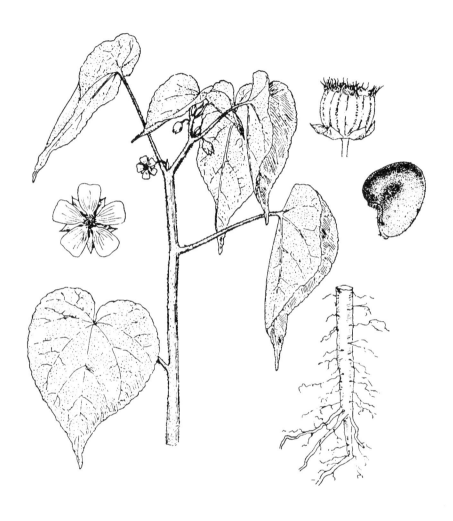

VELVETLEAF, Indian mallow (*Abutilon theophrasti* Medikus). Mallow family. An annual introduced from Asia that reproduces by seed. The entire plant is velvety because of a covering of soft hairs. Stems are erect, sparingly branched, and up to 7 feet tall. Alternate leaves are heart-shaped, pointed at the apex, and up to 5 inches or more wide on slender petioles nearly as long as the blade. Flowers solitary, mostly in upper leaf axils, about 3/4 inch across, with five yellow petals, each notched at its tip. Fused stamens form a tube in the center of the flower. Seed pods are round with 10 to 15 arranged in a disk about 1 inch across. Each pod contains three to nine egg-shaped, somewhat flattened, rough, gray-brown seeds, about 1/8 inch long.

SPURRED ANODA [*Anoda cristata* (L.) Schlect.]. Mallow family. A slightly hairy, erect annual that branches at the base and grows up to 3 1/2 feet tall. Alternate leaves are 1 1/2 to 3 inches long with triangular to lanceolate but still generally triangular blades. They are quite variable even on a single plant. Flowers solitary on long peduncles arising from the axil of the leaf petiole. The purple- red calyx with triangular, pointed sepals is obvious under each fruit. Petals are pale blue to lavender, commonly triangular with narrow end at point of attachment. Carpels 8 to 20 united around a central axis, dark green, and conspicuously beaked with an elongated dorsal spur. The dry fruit splits into two parts with the firmer dorsal part enclosing the hairy seeds. May have been present in Colorado for several years but only noticed as a weedy invader in the 1990s.

BUFFALO GOURD, wild gourd (*Cucurbita foetidissima* H.B.K.). Cucumber family. This native perennial reproduces by seed. The thick, perennial root is carrot-shaped and up to 6 inches or more across, 5 feet or more long with a yellow interior. Trailing stems root at joints, can be 15 to 25 feet long and form large patches, or may climb by tendrils. Leaves are thick, triangular to ovate but sometimes heart-shaped at the base. They are irregularly toothed, rough on top, gray-hairy underneath and 4 to 12 inches long. Flowers are monoecious, borne singly in leaf axils, 3 to 4 inches long, nearly as wide, and bell-shaped with yellow, 5-lobed, recurving petals. Staminate flowers have long peduncles. The fruit is a round smooth gourd, 3 to 4 inches in diameter, variegated yellow and green, with bitter flesh, and containing many pumpkin like, white, oval, flattened seeds each about 3/8 inch long. The plant has a disagreeable odor when bruised. It cannot withstand cultivation. It is found in southeastern Colorado.

ROCKY MOUNTAIN BEEPLANT, pink cleome, stinking clover (*Cleome serrulata* Pursh). Caper family. This native annual reproduces by seed. The erect, smooth stem branches above and is 1 to 3 1/2 feet tall. Leaves are alternate and three-parted. Leaflets are lance-shaped to oblong and pointed. The numerous flowers are red-purple, sometimes pink or white and very showy with four petals each about 1/2 inch long. Sepals are united for 1/2 to 2/3 of their length and persist in fruit. Racemes are greatly elongated. Seed pods are very slender, pointed, 1 to 2 inches long, crowded with seeds, on long slender stalks, and they droop at maturity. Seeds are 1/8 inch long, grooved, rough and yellow-brown. It is an excellent honey plant and the flowers yield nectar at a time when other blossoms are not plentiful. It was used by Indians of the southwest in making pottery paint. It grows in dry soil over the entire state from 3,500 to 8,500 feet.

BLUE MUSTARD, beadpodded mustard [*Chorispora tenella* (Pallas) DC.]. Mustard family. This introduced, ill-smelling, annual reproduces by seed. It is erect with slightly hairy stems 6 to 20 inches tall that branch from the crown. Slightly hairy lower leaves are alternate, sharply incised, narrow, 1 to 4 inches long with toothed margins. Upper leaves are lanceolate, oblong, petioled and less sharply segmented. Flowers are 4-petalled, small and purple to blue in color; rarely white. Fruits (siliques) are slender, pointed, 1 to 1 1/2 inches long, with a prominent beak about 1/3 as long as the pod. They are restricted between seeds and separate at maturity into hard, indehiscent, tan-brown, 2-seeded sections about 1/10 inch long. In spring bluish-purple, bad smelling areas are very evident. It is found throughout Colorado up to 9,500 feet.

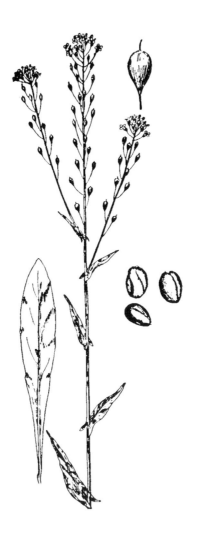

SMALLSEED FALSEFLAX, small-fruited falseflax, little-seed falseflax (*Camelina microcarpa* Andrz. ex DC.). Mustard family. An annual introduced from Europe that reproduces by seed. The slender, erect plants grow 1 to 3 feet high. The stem is hairy, at least below, and simple or with a few elongated branches. Leaves are alternate with lower ones lance-shaped and hairy, and upper ones with pointed, clasping, basal lobes. Flowers are small and light yellow. Racemes grow up to a foot long and bear small pear-shaped pods, each about 1/4 inch long and strongly margined. The small seeds are oblong, ridged on each side, brown-yellow, and about 1/24 inch long. It is widely scattered over Colorado up to 7,500 feet.

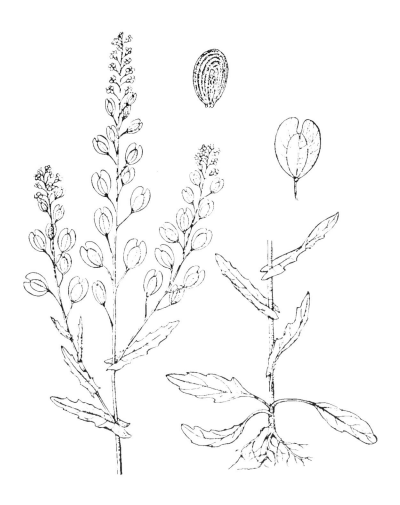

FIELD PENNYCRESS, fanweed, Frenchweed, stinkweed *(Thlaspi arvense* L.).
Noxious. Mustard family. This native of Asia was introduced from Europe. It is an
annual or winter annual that reproduces by seed. Solitary or bunched stems are erect,
smooth, bright green, 6 to 24 inches tall and simple or branching at the top. Leaves
are alternate with the upper ones lance-shaped with entire or irregularly toothed
margins. Inflorescence is a raceme with small, white four-petalled flowers. Circular
fruits are about 1/2 inch in diameter, round, flat, winged, with a deep notch at the
top. Seeds are dark red-brown to black, small, flattened egg-shaped, with fine ridge
and about 1/12 inch long. It can give a bad flavor to milk when eaten by cows, and
the presence of its seeds in wheat renders it undesirable for flour. It is weedy in grain
fields and is especially prevalent in the northwestern United States. It is found
throughout Colorado from 4,000 to 9,500 feet.

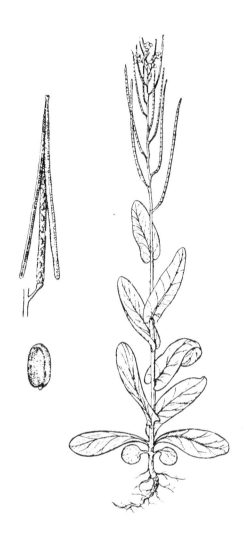

HARESEAR MUSTARD [*Conringia orientalis* (L.) Dumort.]. Mustard family. This weed was introduced from Europe and is an annual, winter annual, or biennial that reproduces by seed. The stem is usually erect, simple or somewhat branching, 1 to 2 or more feet high and covered with a white bloom. Leaves are alternate, light green, 2 to 4 inches long, blunt at the apex. Upper leaves are oblong, entire, broadly rounded above and clasp the stem. Small, pale yellow flowers are in racemes. Fruits (siliques) are numerous, slender, four-angled, and 3 to 4 inches long. Seeds are red-brown, oval, 1/10 inch long, and marked with shallow minute pits. It grows in grain fields and is widely distributed, especially in northwest United States. It is scattered over Colorado, except in the southwest, from 4,000 to 7,000 feet.

INDIAN MUSTARD   **BLACK MUSTARD**

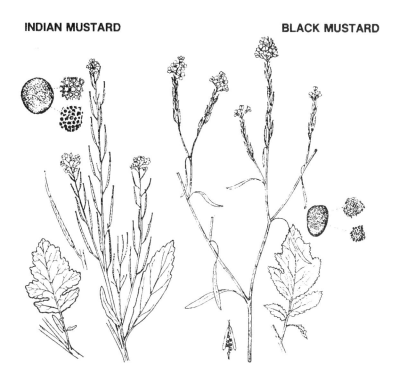

INDIAN MUSTARD *[Brassica juncea (L.) Czern. & Coss.]*. Noxious. This annual, winter annual, or biennial was introduced from Asia and reproduces by seed. It is erect, 1 to 4 feet high, smooth or slightly hairy with only a few branches. Leaves are alternate and pale green. Lower leaves are large and irregularly dentate and petioled. Upper leaves are smaller, lance-shaped, and short-petioled or sessile. Leaves are glabrous and often glaucous. Flowers grow at tips of fruiting stems, are bright yellow, and 1/2 to 3/4 inch across. Fruits (siliques) are erect, 1 to 2 1/2 inches long, with a slim empty beak, one-fourth the length of the pod. Seeds are small, round, red to brown with a netted surface and are up to 1/12 inch in diameter. It is widely distributed but more prevalent in northeastern U.S. It is found in north-central Colorado from 4,500 to 7,500 feet.

BLACK MUSTARD *[Brassica nigra* (L.) Koch] Noxious. Mustard family. Black mustard, introduced from Europe, is an annual that grows erect from 2 to 6 feet tall with branching. It is smooth above to rough hairy below. Leaves are 2 to 10 inches long and 1 to 6 inches wide, all petioled, alternate, with lower ones being divided with a large terminal lobe and a few small lateral ones. Upper leaves are entire and narrow. Flowers are erect, bright yellow and about 1/4 inch across. Seed pods are hairless, appressed to the stem, somewhat four-sided, 1/2 to 1 inch long with a short slim beak and a short (less than 1/4 inch) pedicel. Seeds are small, about 1/16 inch in diameter, round-oval, dark brown and pitted. It grows in grain fields. Black mustard is less troublesome than Indian mustard and not common in Colorado. It is found in the eastern half of Colorado from 4,500 to 8,000 feet.

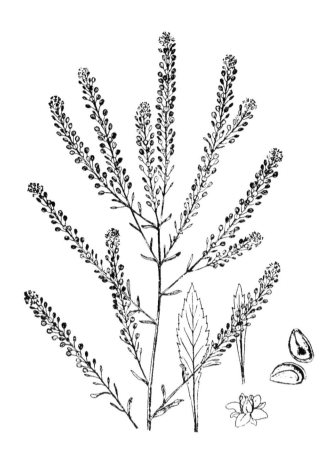

GREENFLOWER PEPPERWEED, peppergrass *(Lepidium densiflorum* Schrad.).
Mustard family. This native of North America is an annual or biennial and reproduces
by seed. Stems have short hairs below and are erect, 6 to 24 inches tall and branch
above. Leaves are alternate with the basal ones spatula-shaped in outline and lobed
with a large terminal lobe. Lateral lobes are small. Stem leaves are sessile or almost
so, mostly sharply toothed with the upper ones entire and linear. Flowers are
numerous, white to green, small, with no or few petals and occur in elongating
racemes. Seed pods are flattened, nearly oval, about 1/8 inch across, notched at the
top and each contains two red-yellow to brown oblong, slightly winged seeds each
about 1/16 inch long. When mature, it may become a tumbleweed. It grows on
prairies and is found in Western States and in north-central, central, and south-
central Colorado from 5,000 to 7,500 feet.

PERENNIAL PEPPERWEED, broad-leaved peppergrass, tall whitetop (*Lepidium
latifolium* L.). This is a perennial from a widely spreading root system. It grows over
1 yard tall and is glabrous or nearly so. Leaves are entire to dentate. Basal leaves are
petioled, oblong, 4 to 12 inches long and 2 to 3 inches wide. Upper leaves clasp the
stem and are smaller than basal leaves. Upper leaves are nearly sessile. Racemes are
many flowered. Sepals are shorter than petals. Petals are spoon shaped and white.

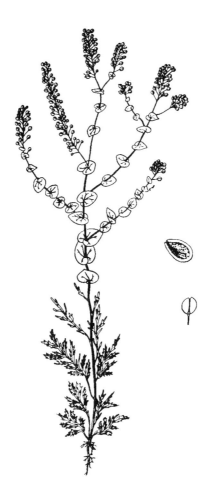

CLASPING PEPPERWEED, perfoliate pepperweed, clasping peppergrass, perfoliate peppergrass (*Lepidium perfoliatum* L.). Mustard family. This annual or biennial was introduced from Europe and reproduces by seed. It has a slender, erect, 6 to 18 inch tall stem that is branched at the top and glabrous to sparsely hairy. Leaves are alternate with clasping lower leaves bipinnatifid into linear divisions. Upper leaves are heart-shaped, smooth, 1/2 to 3/4 inch across, deeply cleft, and the rounded basal lobes clasp the stem and overlap behind it. Flowers have white to yellow petals longer than sepals. They are on slender pedicels in racemes that are 2 to 4 inches long when mature. Seed pods are round, flattened, notched at top, each containing two red-brown, somewhat roughened, wing-margined seeds, each 1/12 inch long. It grows in grain fields and pastures in Western States and over the western half of Colorado up to 8,500 feet.

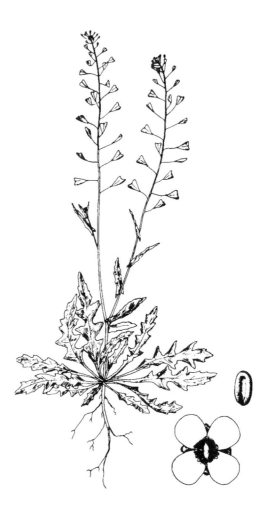

SHEPHERD'S-PURSE [*Capsella bursa-pastoris* (L.) Medicus]. Mustard family. This annual or winter annual was introduced from Europe. It reproduces by seed. Slender to multiple stems are erect, branching, 4 to 20 inches tall, hairy below and smooth above. Leaves are alternate with the basal ones usually lobed and forming a rosette. Upper leaves are few, lance-shaped, clasping, toothed or entire, with small pointed lobes at the base. Flowers are white, small, and usually found at the ends of elongated racemes. The flattened pods are inverted triangles, heart-shaped at top, about 1/3 inch long and grow on slender pedicels. Seeds are very small, oblong, yellow-brown with a single ridge on each side and about 1/32 inch long. It grows throughout the temperate world and is very common in Colorado up to 9,000 feet.

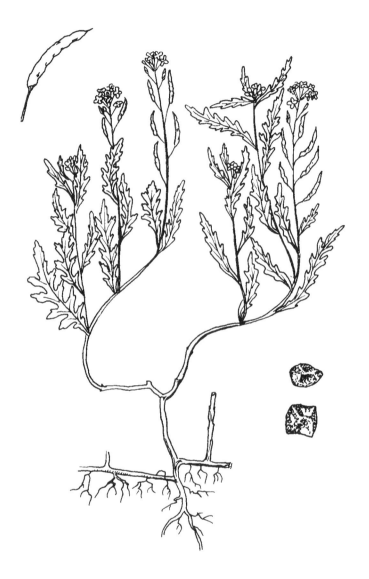

SPREADING YELLOWCRESS [*Rorippa sinuata* (Nutt.) A.S.Hitchc.]. Mustard family. A native, creeping perennial that reproduces by seed and rhizomes. Stems are numerous, diffuse, branched, 4 to 16 inches long, sparsely to densely pubescent, and decumbent to prostrate. Leaves are alternate, about 2 to 3 inches long, oblong, pinnatified into obtuse or acute lobes, partly clasping to non-clasping, each lobe entire to minutely toothed. The numerous flowers are yellow and small in terminal and axillary racemes. Seed pods are slender, sometimes curved, 1/3 to 1/2 inch long and grow on slender fruiting pedicels that are glabrous to densely pubescent with vesicular trichomes. It forms bunches in dry or moist soil throughout Colorado from 3,500 to 7,500 feet.

91

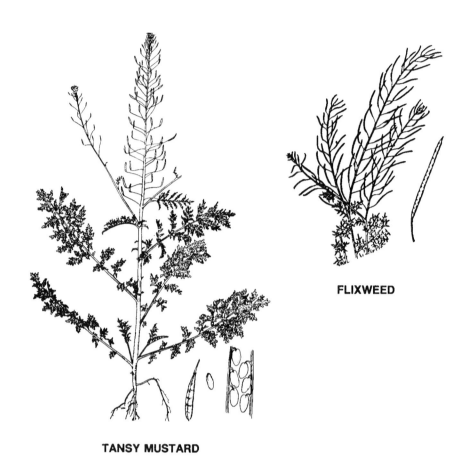

FLIXWEED

TANSY MUSTARD

PINNATE TANSYMUSTARD *[Descurainia pinnata* (Walt.) Britt.]. Mustard family. A native, annual or winter annual that reproduces by seed. The plant is sparsely pubescent to densely covered with fine, white hairs with usually branched trichomes. The stem is erect, branched or simple, and branched above and 4 to 30 inches high. Basal leaves are alternate, 2 to 4 inches long, deeply pinnatified to give a lacy appearance. Upper leaves gradually reduced in size and usually simply pinnate. Flowers are small, whitish to bright yellow, and occur in small clusters at the tips of elongated racemes. Seed pods are on pedicels and are oblong, compressed, 1/4 to 3/4 inch long and nearly the same length or shorter than their pedicels. Seeds are small, up to 1/16 inch long, oblong, dull red, and in two rows in the pod. It is widely distributed and one of the first weeds to appear in spring. There are several subspecies. It is scattered over Colorado up to 8,000 feet.

FLIXWEED, tansy mustard *[Descurainia sophia* (L.) Webb ex Prantl]. This annual or winter annual was introduced from Europe, and is similar in appearance to tansy mustard. It grows to only about 24 inches but the primary way to distinguish it from pinnate tansy mustard is the seed pods. The (siliques) are longer (1/2 to over 1 inch) cylindrical and longer than their pedicels. It is widespread over the state.

TUMBLE MUSTARD, Jim Hill mustard, tall mustard *(Sisymbrium altissimum* L.).
Mustard family. An annual or winter annual introduced from Europe that reproduces
by seed. Erect, smooth stems are simple below, often hairy below, and freely
branching above and grow 2 to 5 feet tall. It is bushy and may break off at the soil
surface to become a tumbleweed. Leaves are alternate; the lower petiolate leaves are
coarse and divided into large lobes while upper ones are much smaller with narrow
lobes. Small flowers are pale yellow and about 1/4 inch across. The numerous
slender fruiting pods are 2 to 4 inches long and produce many seeds. Seeds are small,
brown, oblong, and usually have a single groove. It is widely distributed and especially
troublesome in northwestern U.S. It is found throughout Colorado up to 8,500 feet.

93

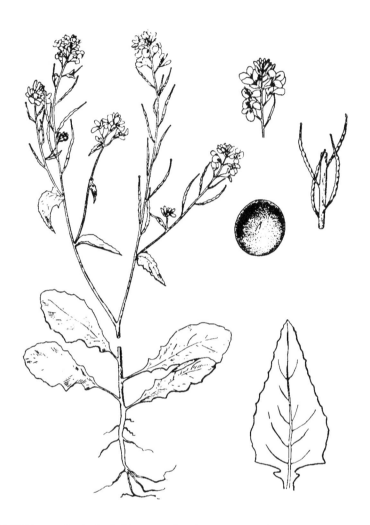

WILD MUSTARD, charlock, field mustard, kaber mustard [*(Brassica kaber* (DC.) L.C.Wheeler) = Sinapis arvensis L.]. Noxious. Mustard family. An annual or winter annual introduced from Europe that reproduces by seed. The stem is erect, 1 to 3 feet high, branching above, and smooth or with scattered stiff hairs below. Leaves are alternate, 2 to 8 inches long, and 1 to 4 inches wide. Lower leaves are deeply lobed while upper leaves are irregularly toothed and may be short-stalked or without a petiole but do not clasp the stem. Flowers are bright yellow and about 3/8 to 1/2 inch across. Hairless seed pods (siliques) are 1 to 2 inches long, oval to round in cross section, and tipped with a four-angled, flattened beak above the uppermost seed. Each valve or half of the silique has 3 to 5 prominent veins. Seeds are small, up to 1/16 inch in diameter, slate-black to black, smooth, spherical, and remain viable in soil for several years. It is distributed throughout the United States and over northern and western Colorado from 4,500 to 8,500 feet.

WHITE MUSTARD (*Brassica hirta Moench*) resembles wild mustard in most ways but its siliques and their pedicels are covered with coarse, spreading hairs especially when young.

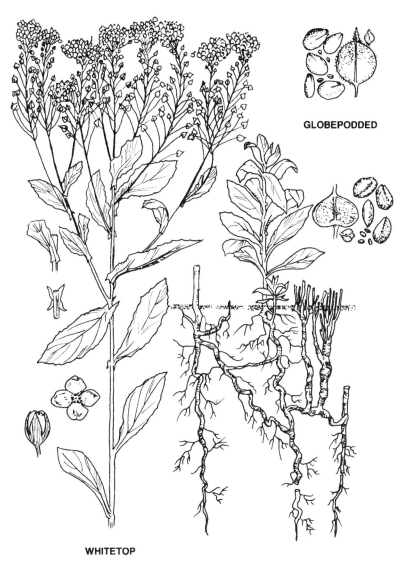

GLOBEPODDED

WHITETOP

HOARY CRESS, whitetop, whiteweed, [*Cardaria draba* (L.) Desv.]. Noxious. Mustard family. This native of Asia was introduced from Europe probably in alfalfa seed. Plants emerge in early spring and flower by midsummer. It is a deep-rooted, creeping perennial that reproduces by seed and horizontal rootstocks. Stems grows up to 2 feet tall and are hairy below. Blue-green to gray-white leaves clasp the stem and are oval or oblong with mostly toothed margins. Each leaf is 1/2 to 2 inches long with blunt ends. Lower leaves have a petiole and basal lobes of upper leaves clasp the stem. Each flower has four small white petals and is about 1/8 inch across. They are numerous in compact flat-top clusters that give the plant its common name. Seed capsules have two, heart-shaped to oval, finely pitted, red-brown seeds each about 1/12 inch long. It grows well on irrigated, alkaline soils of the West. It is found in several sections of the United States, especially in the Rocky Mountain region and on the West Coast. It occurs in cultivated areas over Colorado from 3,500 to 8,500 feet. The variety repens has definitely lens-shaped instead of heart-shaped seed pods, but intergradations are so common as to question the value of the distinction.

HAIRY WHITETOP, globepodded whitetop, whitetop [*Cardaria pubescens* (C.A.Mey.) Jarmolenko]. Noxious. This species is characterized by globose, somewhat smaller, finely hairy pods that remain inflated and globular and take on a purple color as they approach maturity. The plant is smaller than hoary cress and not quite as coarse. There are so many intergradations with *C. draba* in Colorado that maintenance of the species is questionable.

SWAINSONPEA, swainsona, Austrian peaweed [*Sphaerophysa salsula* (Pall.) DC.].
Noxious. Pea family. This weed was introduced from Europe but is a native of Asia. It
is a creeping perennial that reproduces by seed and extensive woody rootstocks. It
forms large patches of erect, 1 to 3 1/2 foot tall stems that freely branch at the
base. Main stems have smaller ascending secondary branches that are round, finely
ridged longitudinally, and sparsely hairy above. Leaves are alternate, pinnately
compound, 2 to 3 inches long, with about 9 to 21 leaflets. leaflets are oval to
oblong, round-pointed at their apex, and somewhat narrowed at the base, 1/4 to 1/2
inch long, short-white-hairy especially lower leaves. Typical pea flowers are red to
purple when dry, 1/2 to 3/4 inch long in racemose clusters each 1 1/2 to 2 inches
long. Seed pods are large, membranous, bladderlike, grooved on one side, about 3/4
inch long and are often bright red and later become pale green. Seeds are small,
round, indented at the point of attachment, olive green, about 1/10 inch in diameter
with about 30 seeds each. It is found in the San Luis Valley in Colorado, about
7,500 feet where it was introduced in alfalfa seed. It has been reported in Weld
County and along the Arkansas River and can become a problem in hay fields.

BLACK MEDIC, hop clover, yellow trefoil *(Medicago lupulina* L.). Pea family. This
annual or possibly short-lived perennial was introduced from Europe. It reproduces by
seed and has a taproot. The 4-angled stem is slender, somewhat hairy, prostrate,
branching at the base, 1 to 2 feet long and spreads in all directions, with many
shorter ascending branches. Trifoliate, leaves are small, alternate, and finely hairy
with oval leaflets. The central leaflet has a short petiole. Yellow flowers are in small
dense racemes up to 3/4 inch long. Seed pods are hairy, thin-walled, kidney-shaped,
slightly twisted, and black when mature. Seeds are ovate, yellow to light brown, and
about 1/24 by 1/12 inch. It is not always a weed because grazing animals eat
Medicago species readily. It has worldwide distribution and is found in Colorado up to
8,000 feet.

HOGPOTATO, Indian rushpea, pignut [*Hoffmanseggia glauca* (Ortega) Eifert]. Pea family. Hogpotato is a native of southwestern United States. It is a creeping perennial that reproduces by seed, horizontal roots, and deep growing, roundish tubers. Erect to spreading, simple or branched stems are slender and 6 to 12 inches tall. Leaves are alternate, 5 to 10 inches long and twice divided into 3 to 5 pairs of well-spaced leaflets that in turn consist of numerous pairs of small, closely spaced, oblong, secondary leaflets, up to 1/4 inch long, with glandular dots. Infloresence is a terminal raceme of loose clusters at stem ends of glandular, pubescent, pea-type flowers, up to 1/2 inch long, with yellow to orange-red petals. Bilaterally symmetrical fruits are flattened and up to 1 1/2 inches long with few to several reddish-brown seeds. Seeds are flattened, egg-shaped and about 1/8 inch long. It is found in southeastern Colorado.

TWOGROOVED MILKVETCH *[Astragalus bisulcatus* (Hook.) Gray]. Pea family. This plant and several relatives extract selenium from soil. Milkvetch also contains other toxins. Twogrooved milkvetch is a perennial that grows from a stout taproot to a height of 10 to 30 inches. Herbaceous stems arise from a woody base and are dark purple in mature plants that form clumps. Opposite leaves are alternate and pinnately compound with 15 to 35 leaflets per leaf. The few to many leguminous, purple or blue (rarely white) flowers occur in axillary racemes at branch ends. The fruit pod is triangular in cross section, with two lateral grooves and contains many seeds. The plant has an unpleasant odor. The keel (lowermost petal) is blunt, in contrast to Oxytropis species in which it is prolonged to a long, distinct point. It is common on Colorado rangeland and grows well in moist alkaline soil.

SILKY CRAZYWEED, white locoweed, locoweed, crazyweed, white woolly loco (*Oxytropis sericea* Nutt. ex T. & G.). Pea family. A native perennial with erect 6 to 16 inch tall, tufted stems emerging from a woody base. It reproduces by seed. Leaflets are opposite, white-gray, and covered with hairs. Leaves usually have at least two distinct shapes and are pinnately compound with a terminal leaflet. Ten to 30 white flowers are borne on a dense raceme above the leaves. Flowers are white in silky crazyweed and pinkish-purple in Lambert or purple crazyweed (*Oxytropis lambertii* Pursh). Color variation is common where the two species intermingle. Flowers occur on a leafless stalk that emerges from the center of the plant. Small. brown, kidney shaped seeds are borne in a firm, leathery, hairy pod. It is found on Colorado rangeland from 4,000 to 9,000 feet. The poisonous principle is called locoine. Horses are most susceptible but other stock can be affected.

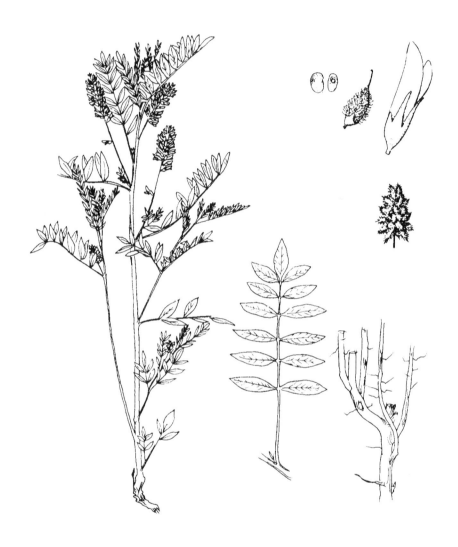

WILD LICORICE, American licorice [*Glycyrrhiza lepidota* (Nutt.) Pursh]. Pea family. This native creeping perennial reproduces by seed and deep, spreading, woody rhizomes. Roots are sweet and somewhat licorice flavored. They can be eaten raw or baked. Stems are erect, simple below and branching above, 1 to 3 feet tall and marked with fine longitudinal lines when dry. Alternate leaves are pinnate with 11 to 19 deeply-veined, lanceolate leaflets. Leaves are sprinkled with small scales when young and corresponding glandular dots when mature. Leaves have petioles up to 1 inch long with a pair of slender, deciduous stipules at the base. Flowers are yellow-white, pealike, and borne close together on short, axillary stems. Burlike seed pods are about 1/2 to 3/4 inch long, brown when ripe, and densely covered with hooked prickles. Seeds are olive-green to brown, oval to bean-shaped and about 1/12 by 1/8 inch long. It grows in open prairies, fields, and meadows and is present in northern and western-United States and in Colorado from 4,000 to 8,500 feet.

PURPLE LOOSESTRIFE, purple lythrum (*Lythrum salicaria* L.). Loosestrife family, a rhizomatous perennial that agressively invades wet, marshy sites. It is often introduced as an ornamental and escapes. It often forms large marshy land colonies that eliminate native species. Stems are 6 to 8 feet tall, four-angled, often pubescent, and woody with basal off shoots. Leaves are simple, entire, opposite or whorled, lanceolate slightly less than 1 inch to 4 inches long and less than an inch wide. Leaves are sessile or nearly so and bases are rounded. Rose-purple flowers are numerous in showy, terminal spikes. There are many ovoid seeds.

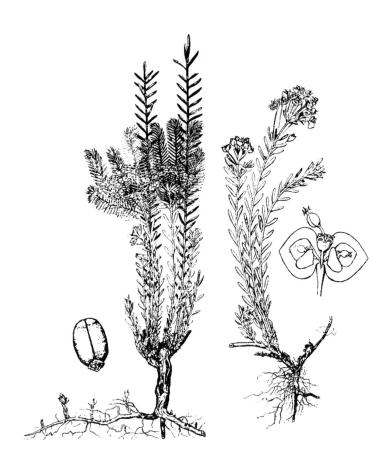

CYPRESS SPURGE *(Euphorbia cyparissias* L.). Spurge family. Cypress spurge, introduced from Europe, is a creeping, densely tufted perennial that reproduces by seed and creeping rhizomes. Stems are thickly clustered with sterile and fertile stems in the same group. They are scaly below and very leafy above, 6 to 12 inches high, with few branches. Branches are terminated by a many-stemmed umbel. Leaves are numerous, crowded, linear, very narrow, 1/2 to 1 inch long, pale green, smooth and numerous. Those at the base of the flowering structures are in whorls, others are alternate. Flowers are small, without petals, and occur in terminal umbels with 10 or more rays. Each flower is enclosed in a top-shaped involucre subtended by pale green, heart-shaped bracts. Seed is rare but when it occurs it is oblong to nearly round, smooth, gray, with a dark line on one side and it is up to 1/12 inch long. Cypress spurge often grows in large, monocultural patches. The plant has a milky latex in all parts. It is present in north-central Colorado up to 5,000 feet. It can be poisonous to cattle when consumed in large amounts.

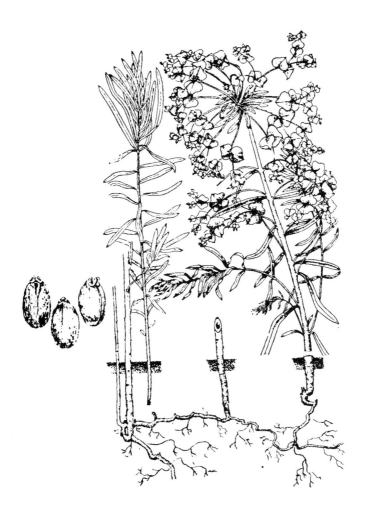

LEAFY SPURGE *(Euphorbia esula* L.). Noxious. Spurge family. Leafy spurge was introduced from Eurasia. It is a creeping perennial that reproduces by seed and from stout rhizomes and rootstocks. It grows erect in clumps and is pale green, 1 to 3 feet high, and unbranched except for flower clusters. Roots have many pink buds. Leaves are alternate, narrowly linear with smooth margins, about 1/4 inch wide, and 1 to 4 inches long. Flowers lack petals or have only remnants, are very small, green-yellow and appear in numerous small clusters, each cluster subtended by a pair of large yellow heart-shaped bracts, all arranged in a conspicuous umbel. Seed pods are three-seeded. Seed is round-oblong, smooth, gray with a dark line on one side and about 1/12 inch long. All plant parts have a milky latex. It is widely scattered throughout the United States and in Colorado's cultivated areas from 5,000 to 6,500 feet. It is not an important weed in most crops but dominates many pastures and wet areas and its range is expanding.

SNOW-ON-THE-MOUNTAIN, white-margined spurge, variegated spurge (*Euphorbia marginata* Pursh). Spurge family. This is a native annual that reproduces by seeds. The stem is stout, erect, up to 3 feet tall, somewhat grooved, usually slightly hairy, unbranched below rays of terminal, 3 to 5 rayed umbel inflorescence. Each ray of the umbel is branched several times. Leaves are ovate, pointed, entire and 1 to 3 inches long. Lower leaves are alternate while upper leaves have white to pink margins. Flowers are small, without petals, each enclosed in a bell-shaped involucre. Seed is a broad oval with a pitted surface, a roughly turbercled ridge on one side and are dull gray to brown, about 1/6 inch long. All plant parts have an acrid, irritating, milky sap, which is considered poisonous. It is scattered throughout Colorado but is more common in the eastern half from 3,500 to 6,000 feet.

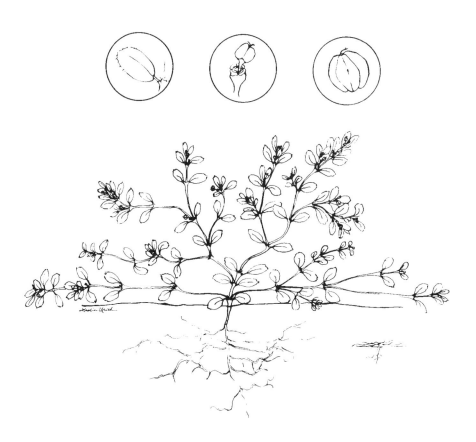

THYMELEAF SPURGE *(Euphorbia serpyllifolia* Pers.). Spurge family. An annual, low-growing plant with smooth to sparingly hairy, highly branched stems up to 15 inches long. Leaves are opposite with small teeth toward apex and commonly have a reddish splotch on the upper surface. The seed pod is sharply three-angled, small with four-angled, white, tan to brown seeds each with a smooth to somewhat roughened coat. It is a common weedy invader of lawns from 4,000 to 7,000 feet elevation.

RIDGESEED SPURGE (*Euphorbia glytosperma* Engelm.). Spurge family. The growth habit is similar to thymeleaf spurge. Leaf margins are entire and stems and leaves are smooth. The capsule is three-angled and wider below the middle. Seeds are sharply four-angled with three to four transverse ridges passing through the angles. It is a weedy invader of lawns. Colorado also hosts ground spurge (*Euphorbia prostrata* Ait.) and spotted spurge (*Euphorbia maculata* L.). The latter has hairy stems and a large purple blotch on each leaf. Ground spurge has hairy stems and leaves but no blotches on leaves. Control methods are not affected by species.

TOOTHED SPURGE (*Euphorbia dentata* Michx.). Spurge family. A native annual that reproduces by seed. The stem is erect or curved and ascending, 8 to 24 inches tall, and somewhat woody below. Leaves of mid-stem opposite, lower ones some-times alternate, 1/2 to 3 inches long, varying in shape from ovate to nearly linear, coarsely toothed, often with a central dark spot, and sparsely to densely pubescent on both surfaces, with prominent veins on underside. Inflorescences of small flowers without petals congested at summit of stems. Each flower enclosed in bell-shaped yellow, nearly sessile involucres in clusters at ends of stems and branches. Three-celled seed capsules are smooth, yellow-green and normally bear three seeds. Seeds are broad, oval, somewhat four-angled, tubercled, gray and about 1/6 inch long. The milky juice of the plant is poisonous but not when the plant is dry. It is found in the eastern half of Colorado from 3,500 to 5,500 feet.

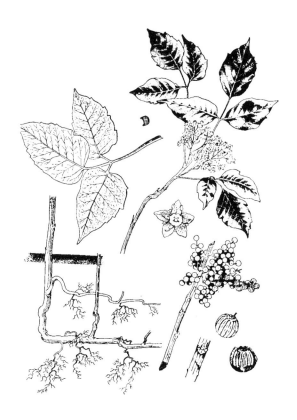

POISON IVY [*Toxicodendron radicans* (L.) Ktze.]. Cashew family. This native creeping perennial reproduces by seed and horizontal roots. It grows as a shrub but is usually less than 3 feet high. Often has aerial roots and creeping rhizomes. Leaves alternate, compound, with three leaflets; a primary character of the plant. Leaflets are 1 1/2 to 8 inches long broadly oval, and pointed at the ends. Leaf margins are usually entire or smooth but sometimes scalloped or toothed. Leaves turn red or orange early in fall. Flowers are in loose, small, green-white panicles. Fruit grows in clusters and is green-white, smooth, waxy, 1/4 inch in diameter, and each contains one hard seed, up to 1/6 inch diameter. The plant phloem, especially in leaves, contains a poisonous, nonvolatile oil that, when in contact with skin, may cause great suffering for some people, evidenced by severe inflammation, itching, and swelling. Smoke from burning plants also may be toxic. It grows in wooded pastures, along fence rows, in mountain canyons, and on hillsides. It is known in north-central, central, and south-central Colorado, but is probably elsewhere from 4,500 to 8,500 feet.

Toxicodendron rydbergii (Small ex Rydb.) Greene also known as poison ivy, does not have aerial roots and forms thickets from much-branched subterranean stolons. Petioles of mature plants are glabrous or nearly so whereas petioles of *T. radicans* are minutely pubescent.

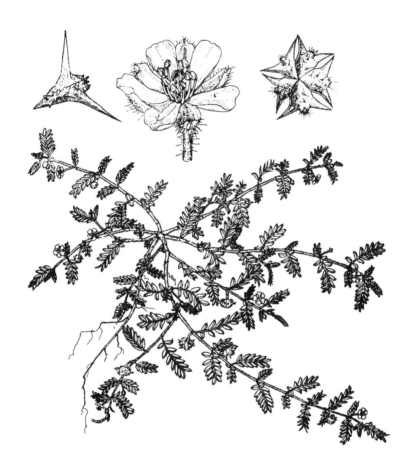

PUNCTUREVINE, bullhead, goathead, Mexican sandbur (*Tribulus terrestris* L.).
Noxious. Caltrop family. This annual, introduced from Europe, reproduces by seed.
It is a prostrate or somewhat ascending, mat-forming plant, with trailing, branched
stems each 1 to 5 feet long and somewhat hairy. Opposite leaves are pinnate, 1 to 2
inches long, with 4 to 6 (rarely 3 or 7) pairs of leaflets, each about 1/4 to 1/2 inch
long and oval. There are lanceolate stipules. Flowers are solitary, yellow, 1/3 to 1/2
inch broad with five petals. The fruit is a hard spiny bur about 1/2 inch broad, which
at maturity breaks up into four or five structures with sharp, sometimes curving
spines. Hard spiny burs damage wool, are bad in hay, and may be injurious to
livestock. Seed remains dormant in soil for several years, making eradication
difficult. It is distributed widely in the United States and Colorado, but is most
common in the eastern half of the state up to 6,500 feet.

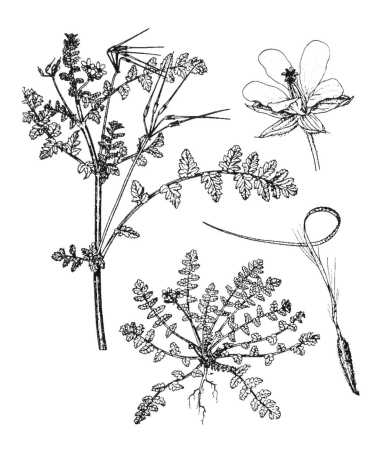

REDSTEM FILAREE, storksbill, alfilaria [*Erodium cicutarium* (L.) L'Her. ex Ait.].
Geranium family. This winter annual, introduced from Europe, reproduces by seed.
Stems are a few inches to 2 feet long, hairy, spreading or nearly prostrate, sometimes erect, and usually grow from a basal rosette. Leaves are hairy, divided into
three to seven pairs of leaflets which are further divided, featherlike, into numerous
finely cut and toothed segments. Flowers on long, 2 to 8 flowered peduncles are
pink to purple in umbels. Fruit has a narrow, pointed beak, up to 2 inches long that
divides into five single-seeded sections at maturity. Each section is sharply pointed at
the seed end and has a long, spirally twisted, sickle-tipped portion of the beak which
facilitates attachment to passing objects and working into the soil. They are undesirable in sheep wool. Seed is elongated, bluntly tapering, brown and about 1/8 inch
long. Under arid conditions it is valued as a pasture plant when young, otherwise it is
a weed in fields and sometimes in lawns. It is scattered over Colorado except in the
extreme east from 4,500 to 7,500 feet.

POISON HEMLOCK, European hemlock *(Conium maculatum* L.). Parsley family. This introduced, European biennial can grow more than 9 feet tall from a stout, white taproot. Highly branched, purple or red spotted stems are ridged and hairless. Shiny green leaves are finely pinnately divided three or four times to give a lacy appearance. Long petioles of lower leaves clasp the stem at their base. Upper leaves have shorter petioles. The base of the stem is not chambered. Entire plant has a distinct parsnip odor. White flowers are borne in many umbrella shaped, terminal clusters. Paired seeds are oval, concave, strongly ribbed, gray-brown, and 1/8 inch long. It grows along ditches, fence rows, roadsides, and field borders and tolerates wet places. All plant parts including the root are poisonous to mammals. It is reported to be the hemlock taken by Socrates. It can be mistaken for parsley and is most common in the western half of Colorado from 5,000 to 9,000 feet.

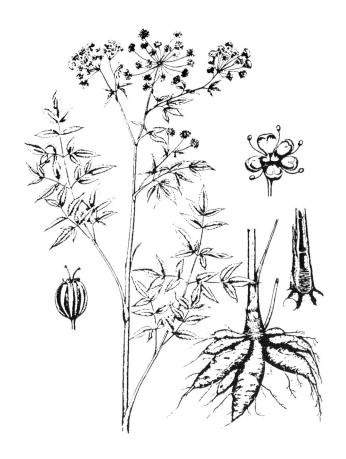

WESTERN WATERHEMLOCK, poison hemlock [*Cicuta douglasii* (DC.) Coult. & Rose]. Parsley family. This native perennial reproduces by seed and tuberous roots. Stems are stout, smooth, hollow, 3 to 7 feet tall, branched at the top, often mottled with purple below. They arise from a cluster of tuberous roots. Leaves are alternate, one per node, petioled, once to thrice compound with leaflets 1 to 4 inches long, long-ovate with margins toothed and veins ending in notches of teeth. Flowers are small, white, in broad, loose conspicuous, terminal umbels borne on long peduncles. The seed is oval to kidney shaped with corky ribs, flattened on one side, brown, and about 1/8 inch long. All parts are poisonous, and horizontally divided tuberous roots are especially so. The plant has caused livestock losses and numerous fatalities in humans. It may be confused with wild parsnip or similar plants, but can be identified by the horizontally divided, swollen chambers revealed by splitting an older stem where it joins the roots, and by the yellow oily drops exuded by cut stems. It grows in moist meadows and along irrigation ditches. It is scattered over Colorado from 3,500 to 8,000 feet.

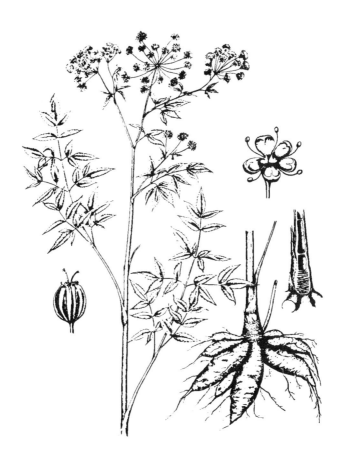

COMMON CARAWAY (*Carum carvi* L.). Parsley family. Common caraway was introduced and escaped from cultivation. It is a biennial (rarely perennial) and the first year's growth is a leafy rosette. One or more stems emerge from a taproot the second year. Stems are erect, branching, smooth, furrowed, usually hollow, 1 to 2 and sometimes 3 feet tall. Leaves are alternate; upper ones with a lacy appearance and finely divided into linear or threadlike seg-ments. Lower leaves are similar but coarser. Flowers are small, white (rarely pink), on up to 1/2 inch long peduncles, and occur in terminal or lateral, loose umbels. Seeds are narrow oblong, more or less curved, 1/8 inch or more long, and brown with five conspicuous tan, linear ribs. It invades mountain meadows in the western half of Colorado from 4,500 to 9,000 feet.

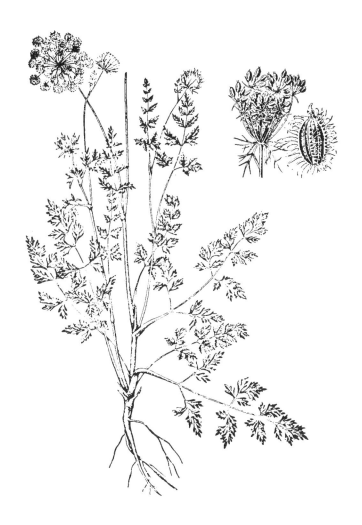

WILD CARROT, Queen Anne's lace (*Daucus carota* L.). Parsley family. Wild carrot, an introduced biennial has a strong carrot odor and reproduces by seed. The first year it forms a rosette of finely, several times divided, feathery leaves from a fleshy taproot. The second year an erect stem grows 1 to 4 feet tall. Stems are hollow and smooth to bristly-hairy. Stem leaves are alternate with the basal ones large, long petioled, pinnatifid, and lacy appearing. Upper leaves are smaller, clasping at the base, and less divided. Leaf margins and veins have short hairs. Flowers are small, white to yellowish, in 3 to 6 inch, terminal umbels which become concave as fruit matures. The central flower of each umbel is normally pinkish or purple. Seeds are gray-brown, oval, flattened on one side, ridged, bristly, and up to 1/8 inch long. It grows in meadows and pastures. It is found in central and south-central Colorado at about 6,000 feet.

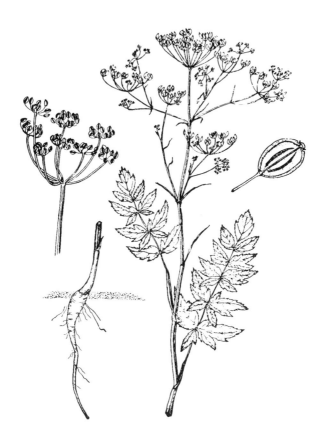

WILD PARSNIP (*Pastinaca sativa* L.). Parsley family. This introduced, aromatic, biennial escaped from cultivation. It reproduces by seed and in the first year a rosette of large upright leaves, up to 15 inches or more long, is formed from a fleshy taproot. In the second year, a 2 to 4 foot tall, branching, hollow, grooved, smooth, erect stem emerges. Stem leaves are alternate and compound. Leaflets are oblong, pointed, and irregularly toothed to lobed. Flowers are small and yellow and grow in large, terminal, rather open umbels. Seeds are straw-colored to light brown, broadly oval, about 1/4 inch long, flattened, with low ribs. The two outside ribs are extended into corky wings. It grows in meadows and pastures. It is not poisonous but is sometimes mistaken for poison hemlock.

COW PARSNIP (*Heracleum lanatum* Michx.) Parsley family. This native perennial is in the same family but differs from wild parsnip. It forms a low-growing rosette with a large, fleshy taproot. Leaves are glabrous to sparsely hairy and commonly 6 to 10 inches broad. They are deeply divided rather than pinnately compound as are other members of the parsley family. Sturdy, grooved, somewhat hairy flower stalks grow 2 to 4 feet tall and bear cream colored, five-petalled flowers. Cow parsnip is found in mountain meadows.

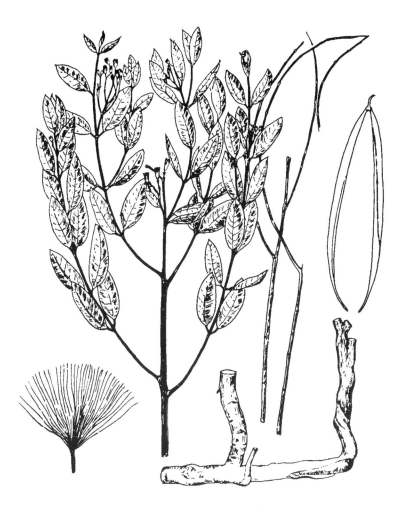

HEMP DOGBANE, common dogbane, Indian hemp dogbane, prairie dogbane *(Apocynum cannabinum* L.). Dogbane family. Hemp Dogbane is a native, creeping perennial that reproduces by seed and rhizomes. It grows up to 5 feet tall with erect, ascending stems and ascending branches. Stems are often red, smooth, tough, and have a milky juice. It frequently forms thicket like growth. Leaves are opposite or whorled, ascending to erect, short petioled to sessile (especially lower), and lanceolate. They are smooth above, pale beneath, and sometimes hairy beneath. Flowers are white, small, bell-shaped, in close terminal clusters, each giving rise to a pair of slender, cylindrical, red-brown up to 6 inch long seed bearing follicles. The numerous seeds are small, linear, brown, about 1/5 inch long, with a tuft of silky white hairs. It grows in cultivated fields, and along ditches, fences, and roadsides throughout Colorado but is most common in the western two-thirds from 4,500 to 7,500 feet.

WESTERN WHORLED MILKWEED [*Asclepias subverticillata* (Gray) Vail]. Milkweed family. A native creeping perennial that reproduces by seed and deep, horizontal roots. Slender, erect, smooth, unbranched stems are 1 to 3 feet tall and occur singly or in clumps. Narrow leaves, 2 to 5 inches long, and not over 3/8 inch wide, grow in whorls of three to four at each node with a very short or no petiole. Secondary clusters of small leaves often occur in leaf axils. Inflorescences are terminal or axillary clusters of green-white petalled flowers. Narrowly lanceolate calyx lobes are green or purple tinged. Erect follicles are 2 to 4 inches long, slender, long-pointed above and short-pointed below and each contains many seeds. Flat, corky-margined, brown seeds are 1/4 inch long and tipped with a tuft of silky hairs for wind distribution. The entire plant is filled with milky juice. It is poisonous at any stage to livestock. It grows in fields, along ditchbanks, roadsides, fence rows, in orchards, and pastures. It is a native of the Rocky Mountains and occurs mostly in western and southeastern Colorado from 3,400 to 7,000 feet.

SHOWY MILKWEED *(Asclepias speciosa* Torr.). Milkweed family. This native creeping perennial reproduces by seed and horizontal roots. The stem is erect, stout, usually unbranched, and grows 2 to 5 feet tall. The plant is usually white-woolly all over with short, downy hairs and has a gray-green color. Leaves are opposite, thick, prominently veined, oblong to elongated egg-shaped, and 3 to 8 inches long. Flowers are purple-pink and borne in large, terminal umbels. Members of the milkweed family have a prominent, erect, to spreading petaloid blade of each flower called a hood. In *A. speciosa* the hood is lanceolate, widely spreading, and 3/8 to 5/8 inch long. In common milkweed (*A. syriaca* L.) hoods are ovate, modestly spreading, and 1/8 to 2/8 inch long. The fruit is a spindle-shaped follicle, 3 to 5 inches long, white-woolly, covered with soft spines, and contains many flat, corky-margined, reddish-brown seeds, each 1/4 to 1/6 inch long and tipped with a tuft of silky hairs. All foliar parts contain a milky juice. It grows in fields and pastures in northern and western United States, and is widespread over Colorado from 3,500 to 7,500 feet.

119

CLAMMY GROUNDCHERRY (*Physalis heterophylla* Nees). Potato or nightshade family. This native, creeping perennial reproduces by seed and horizontal roots. Stems come from a deeply buried persistent base and are erect, hairy, 1 to 2 1/2 feet tall with widely branching, bushy tops. Plant pubescence is varied. Leaves are alternate, broadly ovate, 2 to 3 inches long with wavy to bluntly toothed margins. Flowers are bell-shaped, yellow with a brown to purple center, 1/2 to 3/4 inch across and are borne singly in leaf axils. The fruit is a round, many-seeded, yellow berry, 3/8 to 1/2 inch in diameter, enclosed in an inflated, bladderlike, 1 to 1 1/2 inch long calyx. Seeds are small, yellow, round, flattened, and about 1/12 inch in diameter. It is a persistent perennial resistant to available control techniques. There is much intergradation with other groundcherry species. It grows on irrigated and nonirrigated land, along ditches, and on roadsides in northeastern Colorado from 5,000 to 7,000 feet.

SMOOTH GROUNDCHERRY (*Physalis subglabrata* Mackenz. & Bush). Smooth groundcherry is similar to clammy groundcherry except stems and leaves are smooth. Upper parts are sparsely hairy. Leaves are narrower, ovate sometimes, with smooth to wavy margins. Seeds are irregularly oval to kidney-shaped, flattened, dull, light yellow, and 1/16 inch long. It is found in northern, western, and southwestern Colorado from 5,000 to 7,000 feet.

PURPLE GROUNDCHERRY (*Physalis lobata* Torr.). Potato or nightshade family. This native creeping perennial reproduces by seed and horizontal roots. Stems are usually purple, 4 to 10 inches long, spreading or prostrate and diffusely branched. Leaves are alternate, oblong, or spatulate, wavy-lobed and thick with prominent veins. Flowers are commonly paired and violet or purple, bell-shaped, about 3/4 to 1 inch across with a rayed white woolly center. The fruit is a berry loosely enclosed in a five-sided, inflated, lantern-like calyx, 1/2 to 3/4 inch long, about as wide and sunken at the base with 10 lines of short hairs at maturity. Seeds are few, flattened, irregularly kidney-shaped, light-colored, rough-pitted and 1/8 inch or more long. It is scattered over the eastern half of Colorado from 3,500 to 6,000 feet.

LONGLEAF GROUNDCHERRY, common groundcherry (*Physalis longifolia* Nutt.). Longleaf groundcherry is similar to smooth groundcherry except that leaves are narrower, lanceolate to linear and four to five times as long as wide. Flowers are usually solitary with yellow petals and a brown center. It is found in the eastern, western and southwestern parts of Colorado from 3,500 to 6,500 feet.

121

JIMSONWEED *(Datura stramonium* L.). Potato or nightshade family. This annual, bad-smelling weed reproduces by seed. The stem is green to purple, smooth or hairy when young, stout, 1 to 5 feet high, simple or branching above, and grows from a thick taproot. Leaves are alternate, 4 to 8 inches long, dark green above, lighter below, thin, smooth, with large veins, pointed-oval in outline, and unevenly toothed to shallowly lobed. Erect flowers on short pedicels are solitary, white or violet, five-lobed, trumpet-shaped, 3 to 5 inches long and 2 inches broad. Anthers are white in white flowers and violet in violet flowers. The fruit found in leaf axils is a capsule, egg-shaped, about 2 inches long, densely prickly, enclosing many dark brown, wrinkled, flattened seeds, each about 1/8 inch across. Children have been poisoned by eating the seeds of this plant and by putting the flowers in their mouths. It is also poisonous to livestock, but seldom eaten. It is found throughout eastern Colorado from 4,000 to 6,000 feet.

MATRIMONYVINE *(Lycium halimifolium* Mill.). Potato or nightshade family. This perennial, an escaped ornamental, was introduced from Europe and reproduces by seed. It is a tall climbing or trailing shrub that sometimes forms dense thickets. Stems are 3 to 9 feet long and usually have spines at the nodes of older growth. Leaves are alternate, narrow, oblong, 3/4 to 3 inches long, solitary at nodes or in clusters on older growth. Flowers are lavender to purple, short trumpet-shaped, and 1/3 to 1/2 inch across, solitary of in clusters of 2 to 4. The fruit is an orange-red oval berry (dries black), 3/8 inch or more long, containing many flat, nearly round, brown-yellow seeds about 1/10 inch in diameter. It is found in north-central, west-central, and central Colorado from 4,500 to 8,000 feet.

BUFFALOBUR (*Solanum rostratum* Dun.). Potato or nightshade family. A taprooted, native annual that reproduces by seed. The stem is 1/2 to 2 feet high, much branched, covered with yellowish, star-shaped hairs and strongly armed with slender yellow spines. Leaves are alternate, 2 to 5 inches long with five to seven irregular lobes and are covered with star-shaped hairs. The leaf petiole, midrib and veins are all prickly. Five to 15, 5-lobed, yellow flowers are 3/4 to 1 1/2 inches broad and occur in open clusters. The fruit is enclosed by the enlarged calyx and is covered with long, sharp spines. Seeds are roundish, flattened, shiny dark brown to nearly black, wrinkled, distinctly rough-pitted and up to 1/10 inch in diameter. It is found mainly in eastern Colorado from 3,500 to 6,000 feet.

SILVERLEAF NIGHTSHADE, white horsenettle, prickly nightshade *(Solanum elaeagnifolium* Cav.). Noxious. Potato or nightshade family. This native creeping perennial reproduces by seed and deep, rootstocks. The entire plant is whitish with a dense covering of very fine star-shaped hairs. Stems are erect, slender, branching, 1 to 3 feet high and usually, but not always, armed with slender, sharp, yellow thorns. Leaves are alternate, narrow, oblong to lance-shaped, 1 1/2 to 4 inches long, 1/4 to 1 inch wide, with entire to wavy margins. Violet or blue (rarely white) flowers grow in clusters are five-lobed, and about 1 inch across. The fruit is a round yellow to reddish berry (often black when mature), 1/3 to 1/2 inch in diameter. Seeds are round, flattened, smooth shiny, but finely granular, light to yellow-brown, and 1/8 inch across. It grows in cultivated fields where it may become weedy.

HORSENETTLE, Carolina horsenettle *(Solanum carolinense* L.). Noxious. This is similar to silverleaf nightshade and the main difference is the leaves that are longer and broader, oblong to ovate, 2 to 6 inches long, 1 to 3 inches wide, irregularly lobed, wavy margined, sparsely stiff-hairy but not whitish-hairy. Flowers are violet to white and the fruit is orange-yellow. Seeds are light to yellow-brown, about 1/10 inch across. It is not common in Colorado.

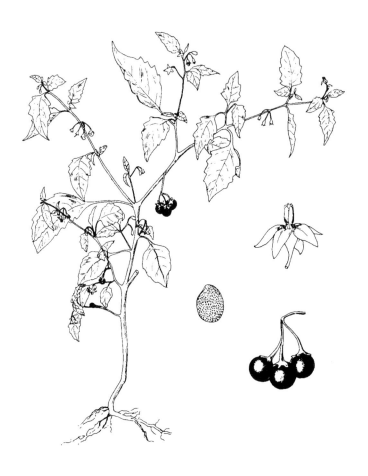

BLACK NIGHTSHADE, poison nightshade *(Solanum nigrum* L.). Potato or night-shade family. This introduced annual reproduces by seed. The stem is smooth or slightly (but not obviously) hairy, and much branched to form a bushy plant 6 inches to 2 feet or more tall. Leaves are alternate, dark green, long, ovate, 1 to 3 inches long, with smooth to irregularly wavy-toothed margins. Flowers are white, about 1/4 inch across, in numerous drooping clusters, 3 to 10 in a cluster, each with a green-yellow, star-shaped center. Each flower gives rise to a 15-60 seeded smooth, round berry, 1/4 to 3/8 inch in diameter, black at maturity with no sclerotic granules. Berries retain the calyx as a covering at the peduncle end. Calyx is small and does not cup the fruit. It is much larger and cups half the fruit in hairy nightshade *(S. sarrachoides* Sendtner). Flattened seeds are oval to nearly circular, about 1/16 inch long, minutely pitted or wrinkled, dull, yellow or nearly white. The entire plant is poisonous, but the berries are especially so when green. It is most important as a weed in field beans and potatoes and as a contaminant of canning peas. It is found in the eastern half of Colorado from 3,500 to 5,500 feet.

126

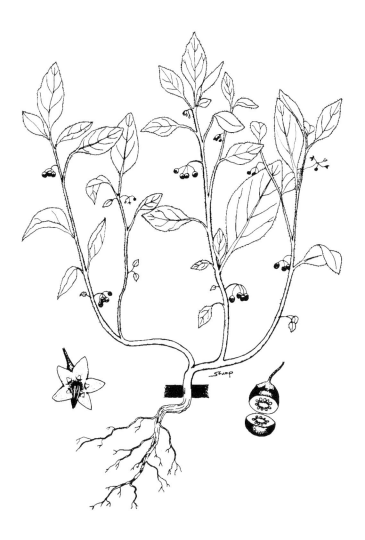

HAIRY NIGHTSHADE, viscid nightshade *(Solanum sarrachoides* Sendtner). Potato or nightshade family. This annual was probably introduced. It reproduces by seed. In most ways it is similar to black nightshade. For control purposes the two can be considered together. The freely branching stem usually grows prostrate but may be up to 2 feet tall. Leaves are alternate, dark green, ovate 1 to 3 inches long and the margins are smooth to irregular. Leaves and stem are moderately to densely pubescent with spreading, mostly glandular hairs. The white corolla is wheel-shaped with a central yellow and purple star, 3/16 to 1/4 inch long with shorter lobes. Flowers give rise to a 10 to 35 seeded, brown to olive-green berry. The spiny, close fitting calyx expands to cover nearly half of the berry. The fruit falls quickly when ripe. The most distinguishing characteristic is the long obvious glandular hairs that make the plant sticky when touched. The species is common where black nightshade is common and they are often confused.

CUTLEAF NIGHTSHADE, wild tomato, three-flowered nightshade *(Solanum triflorum* Nutt.). Potato or nightshade family. This native annual grows from fibrous roots and reproduces by seed. The plant is slightly hairy or smooth. Stems are branched from the base, spreading, 4 inches to 2 feet tall and sometimes erect. Leaves are 2 to 4 inches long, deeply lobed with rounded indentations and pointed at the apex with some pubescence. Seven to nine lobes are somewhat pointed. Flowers are white, 1/3 to 1/2 inch across and usually in groups of two or three (rarely one). The fruit is a round, smooth, usually green berry, 1/3 to 1/2 inch in diameter. Seeds are ovate, much flattened, light brown, finely pitted, and about 1/12 inch long. It is found over Colorado from 3,500 to 9,000 feet.

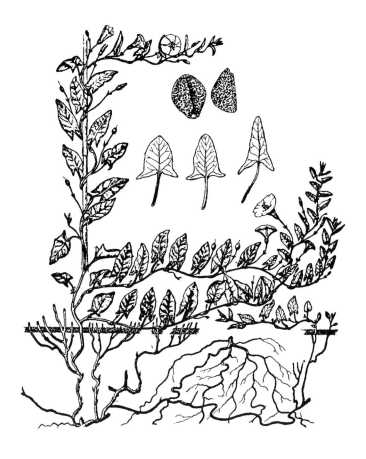

FIELD BINDWEED, European bindweed, wild morningglory, small-flower morningglory, creeping-jenny, (*Convolvulus arvensis* L.). Noxious. Morningglory family. This creeping perennial was introduced from Europe to Eastern U.S. about 1790. It reproduces by seed and horizontal roots. Stems are smooth, slender, slightly angled, 1 to 4 feet long, and spread thickly over the ground or twine around erect plants or other objects. Leaves are alternate, 1 to 2 inches long with great variation in shape. They are more or less arrow-shaped with spreading, pointed, or blunt lobes at the base. Flowers are bell- or trumpet-shaped, white or pink, and about 3/4 to 1 inch in diameter with two small bracts about 1 inch below each flower. The fruit is a small, round capsule, usually four-seeded. Seeds are dull brown, roughened by fine tubercles, pear-shaped, flattened on two sides, round on the other, and about 1/6 inch long. It grows in cultivated fields throughout the United States and world. It is widespread in Colorado from 4,000 to 8,000 feet.

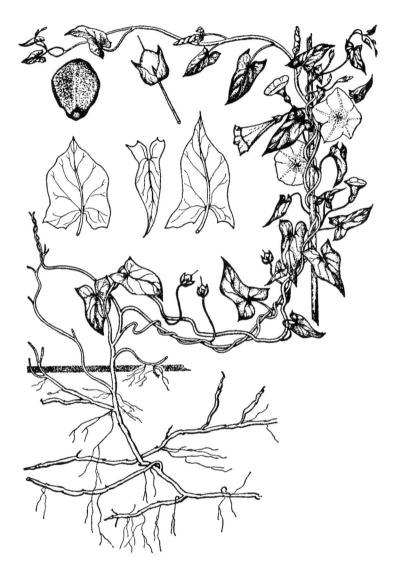

HEDGE BINDWEED, wild morningglory, large-flower morningglory, [*Calystegia sepium* (L.) R. Br.]. Morningglory family. A native creeping perennial that reproduces by seed and elongated rhizomes. It is similar to field bindweed, but larger in all respects. Stems are cylindrical to slightly angular, smooth or slightly hairy, trailing or twining, and 3 to 10 feet long. Leaves are alternate, long-petioled, triangular with the tip and basal lobes pointed but not flared. Flowers are usually solitary in leaf axils, white or tinged with rose or pink, trumpet- or bell-shaped, large, 1 to 3 inches long, 1 1/2 to 2 inches broad, and enclosed at the base by two large clasping bracts that distinguish it from field bindweed. Seeds are black to dark brown, angular, pear-shaped, minutely roughened, and 1/5 to 1/4 inch long. It is distributed over Colorado from 3,000 to 8,500 feet but is less prevalent than field bindweed.

DODDER *(Cuscuta* spp.). Noxious. Morningglory family. Some species of dodder are native to Colorado whereas others have been introduced. It is an annual that reproduces by seed. It is parasitic and nearly lacking in chlorophyll. It grows from seed in the spring as slender, upright, yellow, waving threads, 2 to 4 inches high, which die if they fail to become attached to a host plant. It is seen on the host plant (upon which it is entirely dependent) as a mass of slender, yellow, threadlike branching stems that twine about the host, becoming attached by many haustoria. Alternate leaves are reduced to minute scales. Alfalfa and clover may be stunted and almost obscured by dodder infestations. Flowers are small, bell-shaped, 5-parted, white to pink and occur in compact clusters at intervals along the stem. The fruit is a two- to four-seeded globular capsule. Seeds are small, oval, gray to red-brown, and vary in size among different species from less than 1/25 to 1/16 inch. Seed is difficult to distinguish in alfalfa or clover seed and difficult to remove in cleaning because of similar size. There are several species distinguished by floral anatomy. In Colorado, dodder is a problem in production of alfalfa and clover seed but is of much less importance in hay production.

HOUNDSTONGUE (*Cynoglossum officinale* L.). Borage family. This biennial with a thick, woody taproot and a musty odor was introduced from Europe but is a native of Asia. It is pubescent throughout and appears as a leafy rosette the first year. It reproduces by seed. The stem is erect, stout, heavy, 1 to 4 feet tall and usually branched above. Leaves are alternate with the basal and lower ones petiolate, broad, oblong to lance-shaped, up to 12 inches long, and 1 to 3 inches wide. Upper leaves are sessile, narrower, pointed, and almost clasping. The whole plant is covered with soft, white hairs. Flowers are red-purple (rarely white) and occur in long, sometimes branched, terminal clusters. The fruit consists of four, barbed, prickly nutlets each about 1/4 to 1/3 inch long. Nutlets break apart at maturity and are spread easily in fur. It is found in Colorado from 5,000 to 9,000 feet.

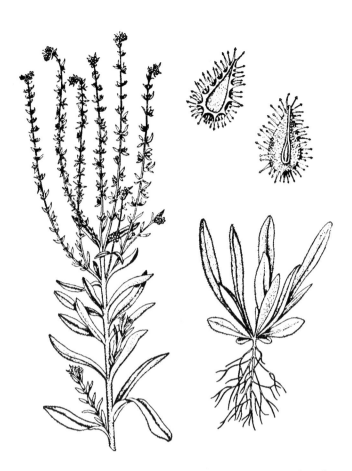

EUROPEAN STICKTIGHT, blue stickseed, hairy stickseed (*Lappula echinata* Gilib.). Borage family. European sticktight was introduced from Eurasia. It is an annual that reproduces by seed. Stems are erect, 1 to 2 feet high, branched above with ascending branches, and spreading hairs. Sessile leaves are linear or narrow-oblong, somewhat blunt, the lower ones spatulate, and gray with soft hairs. Flowers are tiny and blue. Seed pods are small burs, about 1/8 inch long, breaking up into four gray to dark brown nutlets whose dorsal face is armed with 2 (sometimes 3) rows of bristles around it. It grows in dry soil and sandy places in the Western Plains and often invades after overgrazing. It is found in northwest Colorado from 6,500 to 7,500 feet.

WESTERN STICKTIGHT [*Lappula occidentalis* (S. Wats.) Greene]. Borage family. This plant strongly resembles European sticktight. Leaves are less hairy and petals are blue or white. Nutlets are slightly smaller with only one row of bristles around the dorsal face

WESTERN STICKSEED, large-flowered stickseed [*Hackelia floribunda* (Lehm.) I.M.Johnst.]. Borage family. This is similar to European sticktight but is a native biennial or perennial that grows up to 5 feet tall. There is one to few stems, branched above and with downward directed, appressed, stiff hairs. Basal leaves are early deciduous and all leaves clasp the stem. Nutlets are much larger; up to 1/4 inch. It is scattered over the western half of Colorado from 6,500 to 10,000 feet.

BLUE VERVAIN, wild verbena (*Verbena hastata* L.). Vervain family. A native perennial that reproduces by seed and short, spreading roots. The stem is erect, four-sided, 3 to 5 feet tall, finely rough-hairy, coarsely grooved and branching at the top. Leaves are opposite or whorled, 2 to 6 inches long, oblong to lance-shaped, pointed, narrow at the base, finely rough-hairy, with toothed margins, heavy veins, and a short, grooved petiole. Flowers are small purple-blue to pink, tubular, five-lobed, and borne on numerous slender spikes, each 2 to 6 inches long, in an upright panicle. Each spike has few blooming flowers and frequently there is maturing fruit below with green buds above. The fruit is a small, dry pod crowded upon the spike, separating into four small, oblong, red-brown seeds with linear ridges on one side and about 1/12 inch long. It grows in moist place, fields, meadows, and roadsides and is found in northeastern Colorado from 3,500 to 5,000 feet.

HOARY VERVAIN (*Verbena stricta* Vent.). Vervain family. A native perennial that reproduces by seed. It is similar to blue vervain but is covered with soft white hairs, and spikes are thicker (1/3 inch or more) and longer (6 to 12 inches). Blue to purple flowers are larger. Seeds are 1/8 inch long, dark or gray-brown. It is scattered in the eastern half of Colorado from 3,500 to 5,500 feet.

WEDGELEAF FOGFRUIT [*Phyla cunefolia* (Torr.) Greene = Lippia cunefolia (Torr.) Steud.]. Vervain family. A native creeping perennial that reproduces by seed. It branches profusely from a woody stem base. Stems are up to 3 1/2 feet long, with short, erect branches and fibrous roots at nodes. Leaves are opposite, sessile, wedge-shaped, 1/2 to 1 1/2 inches long, with two to eight sharp teeth above the middle. Leaves are rarely entire and usually somewhat pointed. Flowers are purple or white and occur in dense, clusters, borne on axillary stems. The fruit is small, dry, and separates into two small, light brown to tan seeds. It grows in the eastern half of Colorado from 4,000 to 6,000 feet.

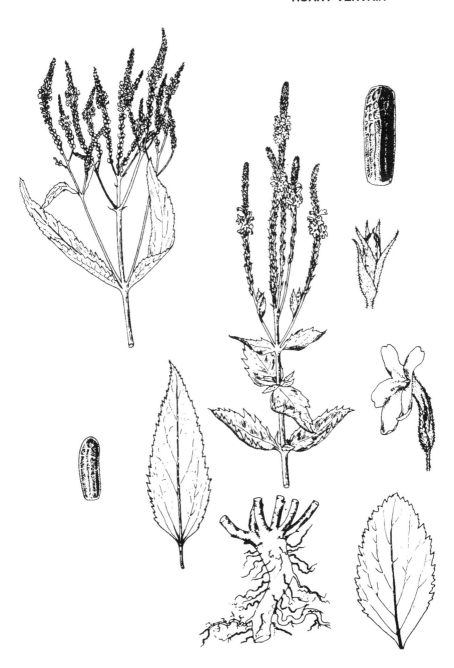

BLUE VERVAIN

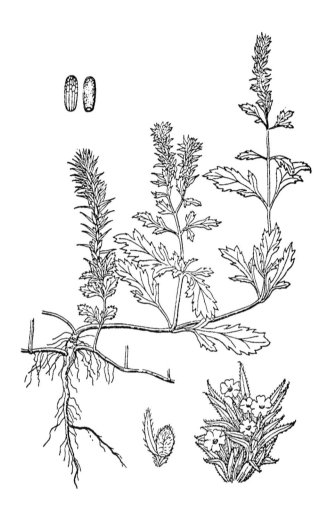

PROSTRATE VERVAIN, bracted vervain (*Verbena bracteata* Lag. & Rodr.). Vervain family. This native annual or short-lived perennial reproduces by seed. Stems are widely spreading, much branched, four-sided, rough-hairy, 6 to 20 inches long and emerge from a single tap root. Branches are prostrate to ascending at tips. Leaves are opposite, small, 3-parted and 3-lobed, 1/2 to 2 or more inches long, variously toothed, and borne on short petioles. Flowers are small, sessile, blue to purple, tubular, in thick compact terminal spikes, 4 to 6 inches long. They are almost concealed by prominent stiff, hairy bracts. Few flowers bloom at a time, frequently resulting in green buds above and mature fruit below. The fruit is a small, dry pod separating into four small, oblong, gray to dark brown seeds that are ridged to netted on one side and about 1/12 inch long. It is scattered over Colorado from 3,500 to 7,500 feet.

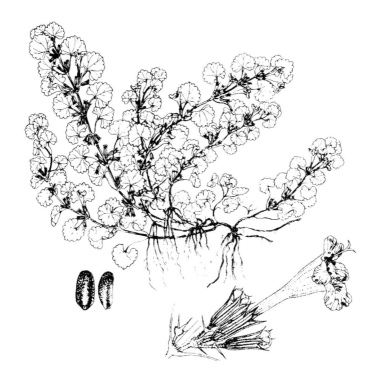

GROUND IVY, Gill-over-the-ground, creeping charley *(Glecoma hederacea* L.). Mint family. A creeping perennial introduced from Europe that reproduces by seed and creeping stems. Stems are square in cross section, 8 inches to 2 feet long, and root at nodes. Leaves are opposite, rounded or kidney-shaped, smooth to sparsely hairy, 1/2 to 11/2 inches across, with scalloped edges, and green on both sides. Upright flowering shoots bear funnel-shaped flowers, about 1/2 to 2/3 inch long, pale purple in small clusters in leaf axils. The fruit separates into four mottled brown seeds each about 1/12 inch long. It grows under moist conditions in lawns and is found in north-central and central Colorado from 5,000 to 6,000 feet. This can be confused with Persian speedwell (*Veronica persica* Poir.). Persian speedwell is an annual with round stems. Lower leaves are paired and upper are alternate. Flowers have four blue petals and are round not funnel shaped. Leaves are similar. Ground ivy leaves are more nearly round and have scalloped edges. Persian speedwell leaves are roughly triangular with toothed margins. A careful look is required to distinguish them.

HEALALL, selfheal (*Prunella vulgaris* L.). Mint family. A native, creeping perennial that reproduces by seed, creeping stems, and short, slender rhizomes. Flowering stems are square, glabrous to hairy, and will grow 2 to 12 inches tall if unmowed. Leaves are opposite, ovate, oblong, or lance-shaped, rarely rounded, 1 to 3 inches long, hairy to smooth and are borne on a long petiole. Flowers vary from almost white to deep purple and occur in compact spikes. Seeds are small, about 1/16 inch long, slightly flattened, brown, slightly rough, and glossy. It is widely distributed in western Colorado from 5,000 to 10,000 feet.

137

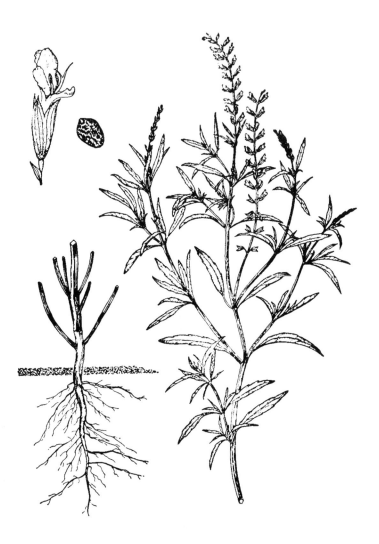

LANCELEAF SAGE, blue sage, Rocky mountain sage, sage mint (*Salvia reflexa* Hornem.). Mint family. This native annual reproduces by seed. The stem is four-sided, leafy, usually much branched above the base, erect or spreading, and 6 to 12 inches high. Leaves are opposite, lance-shaped or oblong, mostly blunt at the apex and narrowed at the base. Leaf margins are toothed or entire, and leaves are 1 to 2 inches long. Flowers are blue, somewhat bell shaped with an extended lower lip, about 1/3 to 1/2 inch long. The lower lip of the flower is twice as long as the upper. Flowers are generally opposite, but sometimes three or four are together in a terminal raceme. The fruit is dry and separates into four light brown seeds with darker brown markings, each about 1/12 inch long. It is common on the plains and scattered over Colorado except in the northwest from 3,500 to 8,000 feet.

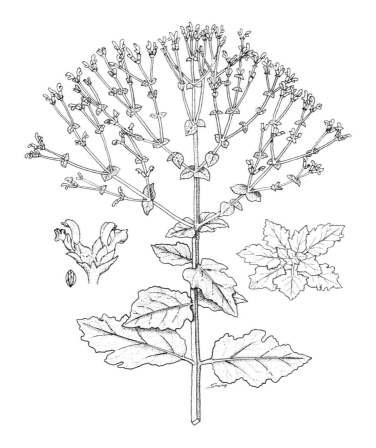

MEDITERRANEAN SAGE *(Salvia aethiopis* L.). Mint family. This aromatic (sage odor), non-poisonous, biennial or short-lived perennial is native to southern and southeastern Europe and is an agressive invader of rangeland. It was first introduced near Susanville, California in about 1892. It grows 2 to 3 feet tall in its second season after developing a 7 to 10 inch diameter rosette of large gray-green to blue-green, wooly leaves the first season. Rosette leaves have indented, irregular margins and a 1 1/2 to 3 1/2 inch petiole. Common mullein rosettes are similar but the leaves have more regular margins, are yellow-green, and lack petioles. Stems are erect, multi-branched, sturdy, 4-angled, with opposite leaves, and a stout taproot. Leaves are white to blue-green, and felt-like when touched. Older leaves tend to lose the covering of hairs to reveal prominent veins and a wrinkled surface. Most leaves are in the basal rosette. Stem leaves become progressively smaller upward with the uppermost clasping the stem and are often reduced to purple-tinged bracts. Lower stem leaves are 4 to 12 inches long, petioled, with coarsely toothed blades. A highly branched panicle bears numerous white to yellow-white flowers in woolly clusters. Each 1/2 inch flower has an upper lip resembling a hooked beak. The pale yellow lower lip is divided into three lobes with the center lobe smaller than the outer lobes. The seed bearing panicle detaches naturally and blows in the wind, like a tumbleweed. Each flower produces four seeds but an average plant may produce as many as 100,000 smooth, brown with darker brown veins, egg-shaped, about 1/8 inch long seeds.

BROADLEAF PLANTAIN (*Plantago major* L.). Plantain family. This fibrous-rooted, simple perennial weed grows from a tough, persistent base of the herbaceous stem. It was introduced from Europe and reproduces by seed. It is smooth or somewhat hairy. Leaves are all basal, with 1-inch-long petioles and a firm texture. Leaf blades are 3 to 7 nerved, ovate to oval, 2 to 12 inches long, with smooth or toothed margins. One to 30 peduncles are 2 to 15 inches tall and bear small, closely clustered, erect inflorescences. Flowers are small and inconspicuous with exerted, purplish, distinctly horned anthers. Seeds are small, dark brown, irregular in shape and 1/16 inch or more long. It is weedy in lawns throughout the U.S. and is distributed in Colorado from 3,500 to 9,000 feet.

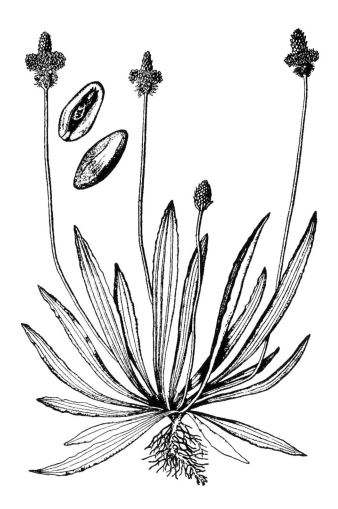

BUCKHORN PLANTAIN, narrowleaf plantain (*Plantago lanceolata* L.). Plantain family. This introduced simple perennial reproduces by seed. Numerous leaves grow directly from the crown of the persistent stem base which is conspicuously tan-woolly at its summit. Leaves are 4 to 12 inches long, narrow (less than 1 1/2 inches wide), 3 to several veined, lance-shaped, and slightly hairy with tufts of hair at the leaf base. Several flowering stalks bear dense cylindrical spikes, 1/2 to 2 inches long, on slender, channeled peduncles each 4 to 18 inches long. Flowers are pistillate, staminate, or perfect, corolla lobes are up to 1 inch long, white, and flowers first appear at the base of the spike and progress upward. Seeds are shiny, brown, oblong, concave on one side, rounded on the other, up to 1/10 inch long and very mucilaginous when wet. It is scattered over the state from 4,500 to 7,000 feet and invades meadows, pastures, and lawns.

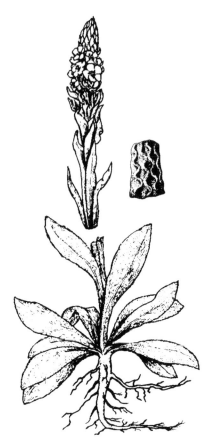

COMMON MULLEIN, Jacob's staff *(Verbascum thapsus* L.). Figwort family. This biennial reproduces by seed and was introduced from Europe but is a native of Asia. It forms a large thick rosette of fuzzy leaves, up to 2 feet across the first year, from which a coarse woolly plant arises in the second year. The stem is 2 to 6 feet tall, stout, erect, simple or with one or a few upright branches near the top. Leaves are alternate with basal ones oblong, 4 to 18 inches long, thick, light green, densely woolly, narrowing toward their base, and maintaining a large, thick rosette on the ground. Upper leaves are gradually smaller, narrow, and more pointed. Inflorescence is a congested spike. Flowers are yellow, 3/4 to 1 inch broad, sessile, and crowded on a long, dense, cylindrical, terminal spike or spikes, 1 to 3 feet long. The fruit is a capsule about 1/4 to 1/3 inch long, cylindrical, and filled with many small angular, pitted brown seeds, each about 1/32 inch long. Livestock will not eat it because of its woolliness. It is scattered over Colorado from 4,500 to 9,000 feet.

MOTH MULLEIN *(Verbascum blattaria* L.). Figwort family. A biennial native of Europe that produces a rosette of leaves the first year and flowers the second. Rosette leaves are dark green, glandular-pubescent above with simple hairs. Leaves often tinged with red, usually shallowly lobed, toothed, and tapering to a short petiole. Leaf charactersitics distinguish this species from common mullein. Leaves of the flowering stem are merely toothed, becoming smaller upward on the stem, sessile, and nearly clasp the stem. The single flower stem is 1 1/2 to 5 feet tall. Flowers are bright yellow, sometimes nearly white, irregular and 5-lobed.

A: Habit – x 0.5; B: basal leaf – x 2; C: flower – x 3 c. corolla, showing stamens: cc, calyx, showing subequal sepals – x 5; D: capsule – x 3 ; E: seeds – x 25.

PURSLANE SPEEDWELL (*Veronica peregrina* L.). Figwort family. This native annual or winter annual reproduces by seed. The stems are numerous, smooth to glandular pubescent, usually much branched, and 3 to 12 inches tall. Leaves are oblong to narrow, rather thick, entire to toothed with lower ones opposite and short-petioled and upper leaves are sessile and alternate. Flowers are solitary in leaf axils, small, and white to blue. The fruit is a heart-shaped, flat pod notched at its apex, about 1/8 inch long and contains numerous seeds. Seeds are small, oval, flattened, glossy, orange-yellow, and about 1/32 inch long. It is widespread in North America and can be found throughout Colorado but mostly in the western two-thirds from 4,500 to 8,500 feet.

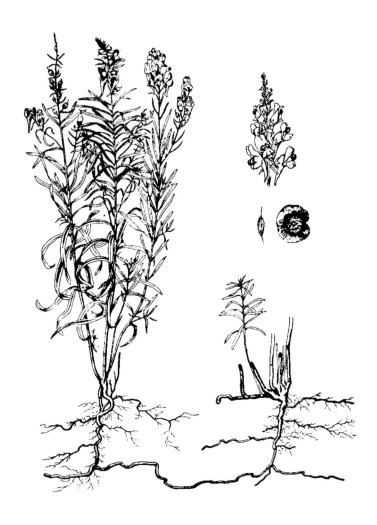

YELLOW TOADFLAX, butter-and-eggs, wild snapdragon (*Linaria vulgaris* Mill.). Noxious. Figwort family. This introduced creeping perennial is an escaped ornamental that reproduces by seed and extensive horizontal roots. Stems are smooth, erect, leafy, often in clumps, and 1 to 2 1/2 feet tall. Numerous pale green leaves are alternate, narrow, pointed at both ends, and 2 1/2 or more inches long. Flowers resemble those of cultivated snapdragon; each has a spur extending below from the lower lip of the corolla. They are about 1 inch long, bright yellow with a bearded, orange throat and occur in terminal, somewhat elongated clusters with the youngest flowers at the tip. The fruit is a brown, globe-shaped, two-celled capsule, 1/4 inch in diameter containing many seeds. Seeds are small, round, rough, flattened, with a papery, notched circular wing, dark brown, and about 1/12 inch in diameter. It is a persistent, aggressive invader in Colorado from 6,000 to 8,500 feet mostly on the Western Slope.

DALMATION TOADFLAX [*Linaria dalmatica* (L.) Mill. = *Linaria genistifolia* ssp. *dalmatica* (L.) Maire & Petitmengin]. Noxious. This differs from yellow toadflax principally in being larger and having differently shaped leaves. Clumps of stems are 3 to 4 feet tall. Waxy leaves are broad, ovate, sometimes heart shaped and upper leaves clasp the stem (an important difference). Seeds are irregular in shape, angular, somewhat flattened, thin-edged, strongly netted, tan-gray and 1/24 to 1/16 inch across. It is not as common, but is more aggressive than yellow toadflax. It is reported in various parts of the state from 5,000 to 6,500 feet.

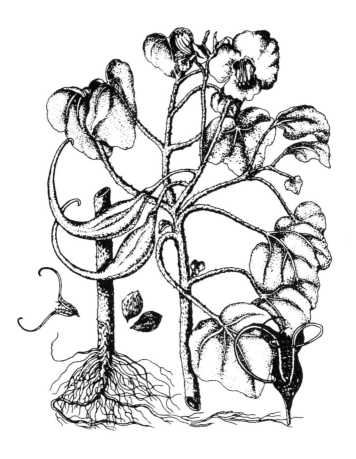

DEVIL'S-CLAW, unicornplant [*Proboscidea louisianica* (Mill.) Thellung]. Unicornplant family. This bad-smelling (horsey odor), native annual reproduces by seed. The stem is stout and much branched and forms a broad spreading or bushy plant, 1 to 3 feet tall that is densely covered with glandular hairs. Leaves opposite or sometimes alternate near the top of the plant, 3 to 12 inches wide (usually slightly greater than their length), kidney-shaped to roundish with wavy to slightly toothed margins. Attractive, large, tubular flowers in open terminal racemes that usually are taller than the foliage, 1 1/2 to 2 inches long. Five lobed corolla becomes bell-shaped, dull-white to purplish throughout, mottled inside with yellow or purple. The inner floral tube is conspicuously reddish-purple spotted and the lower portion is yellow striped. Bivalved fruit is 2 to 4 or more inches long with a curved beak longer than the body. At maturity the pod dehisces and divides into two opposite incurved claws with an inwardly hooked, pointed tip, to form an ice-tong like structure which may become attached to livestock or equipment. Seed is somewhat flattened, ovate to oval, irregularly rough, brown-black and up to 3/8 inch long with many in a pod. The entire plant exudes a sticky substance. It is found in the eastern haft of Colorado from 3,500 to 4,500 feet.

CREEPING BELLFLOWER, rover bellflower, creeping harebell, (*Campanula rapunculoides* L.). Bellflower family. This creeping perennial, introduced from Eurasia, is an escaped ornamental that reproduces by seed and slender rhizomes. The plant is characterized by fleshy, frequently bifurcated taproots. Stems are simple or sparingly branched, commonly purplish, numerous, 1 to 4 feet tall, smooth or slightly hairy. Leaves are somewhat rough, alternate, pointed, irregularly toothed, 2 to 4 inches long, with the lower ones being heart-shaped and the upper ones sessile, narrow, ovate and gradually smaller toward the top of the plant. Purple flowers are attractive, bell-shaped, about 1 inch long, nodding, in a loose elongated terminal cluster with the youngest flowers at the tip. Petals have generally triangular tips. Lowermost flowers have short pedicels and are subtended by obvious bracts, upper flowers have shorter pedicels and reduced bracts. The fruit is a three-celled globular capsule. Seeds are very small, numerous, chestnut-brown, lustrous, oval, round on both sides, and about 1/24 inch long. It is weedy in lawns and perennial flower plantings and is widely distributed in Colorado.

SUNFLOWER = ASTER FAMILY *(Asteraceae* = Compositae) Many weeds, ornamental, and native plants belong to the sunflower family. A brief description of the family is given to provide an understanding of the flower parts essential for species identification. Some terms are unique to this family. Members of the Asteraceae have small flowers grouped in floral structures that resemble single, large flowers. These are surrounded by one or more rows of bracts that vary in form, arrangement, texture, and number and increase the resemblance to a single flower with its subtending calyx. Five stamens are inserted on the petals and united laterally to enclose the style that branches above into two arms. The petals are united into a corolla that may be tubular with five short terminal lobes of equal length, or ligulate, with one side of the corolla tube prolonged and strap-shaped. The floral structure may contain only ligulate flowers as in dandelion, tubular flowers in the center and ligulate flowers at the margin as in sunflower, or only tubular flowers as in ragweed. Plants with only ligulate flowers usually have milky latex in leaves and stems; those with only tubular flowers lack latex. Seeds of the Asteraceae are, technically speaking, achenes = dry indehiscent fruits. Seeds are frequently crowned by a pappus, a modified calyx, which differs among species. It may consist of scales, bristles, simple or plumose hairs in one or more rows, or these may be absent. Illustrations of a number of seeds with attached pappus are on the next page and show some of the variations in seeds and pappus.

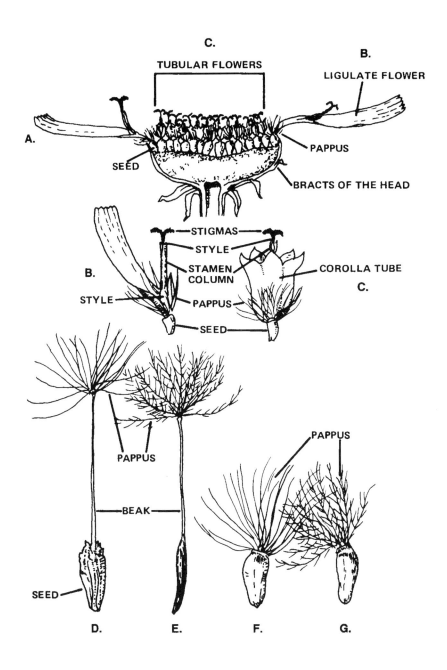

A. Cross-section of the flower head of the Asteraceae with tubular and ligulate flowers; B. Ligulate flower; C. Tubular flower. Seeds of several species showing different types of pappus: D. Simple pappus on a beaked seed - dandelion, *Taraxacum officinale*; E. Plumose pappus on a beaked seed - common catsear, *Hypochoeris radicata*; F. Simple pappus - plumeless thistle, *Carduus acanthoides*; G. Plumose pappus - Canada thistle, *Cirsium arvense*.

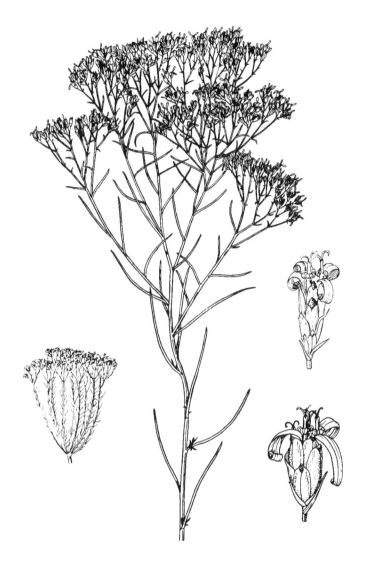

BROOM SNAKEWEED, broomweed, perennial snakeweed, turpentine weed, stinkweed [*Gutierrezia sarothrae* (Pursh) Britt. and Rusby]. Sunflower family. Aster tribe. Snakeweed is a native, perennial, densely branched, resinous shrub, which grows up to 2 feet tall and is woody at the base. Crowded, stiff, bushy stems grow new from the crown each year. There are numerous, herbaceous, leafy branches from which the lower leaves are shed at maturity in northern but not in southern states. Branches are ascending, hairless, and ridged. Narrow leaves are green, alternate, linear, 3/4 to 2 inches long, slightly rolled toward the center, with smooth margins, and grow on the upper part of the stem. Yellow disk and ray flowers combine in small, round flowers that occur singly at the tips of many upper branches. Oval fruit is covered with scales. Achenes have a pappus of 8 to 10 acute scales. It is found on heavily grazed rangeland from 4,000 to 10,000 feet.

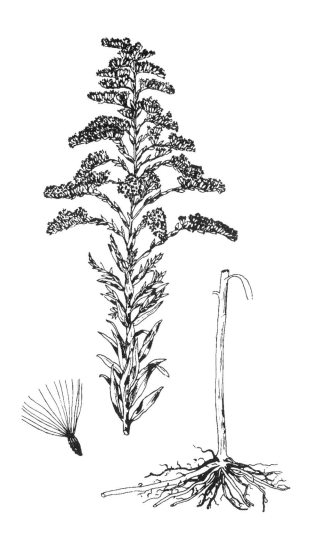

CANADA GOLDENROD *(Solidago canadensis* L.). Sunflower family. Aster tribe. This native, creeping perennial reproduces by seed and horizontal roots. The stems are erect, rough, leafy, 2 to 4 feet tall and arise singly to form clumps or patches. Leaves are alternate, narrow, 2 to 4 inches long, without petioles, 3-nerved, usually toothed and densely hairy above but smooth on the underside. The inflorescence is paniculate with prominent recurved branches directed to one side. Yellow flowers are densely assembled in an extensive, showy, display. Achenes are small, oblong, tapered, about 1/16 inch long with hairy pappus at the tip. It is scattered over Colorado from 3,500 to 9,000 feet. There are several other species in the state.

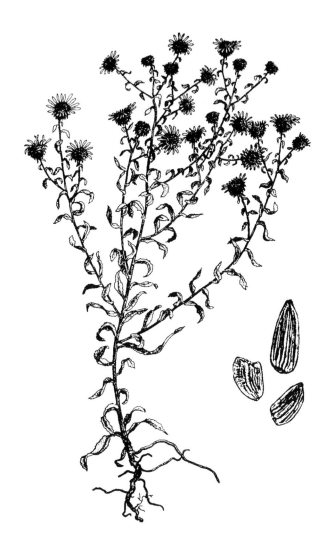

CURLYCUP GUMWEED, rosinweed, gumweed [*Grindelia squarrosa* (Pursh) Dunal]. Sunflower family. Aster tribe. Gumweed, a native biennial or short-lived perennial, reproduces by seed. The stem is smooth, erect, 1 to 3 feet tall and freely branching. Leaves are alternate, 1 to 3 inches long, oblong or spatulate, somewhat blunt, with saw-toothed margins. Leaves are dotted with glands that exude a sticky resin. Flowers are bright yellow, 1/2 to 1 inch across, borne singly on branch ends, and sticky from resin. Green, recurved bracts that subtend each flower are also very sticky. Achenes are four-angled, cream-colored, oblong, rather deeply ridged, and about 1/8 inch long. It is scattered over Colorado, except in the extreme south, from 4,500 to 5,000 feet.

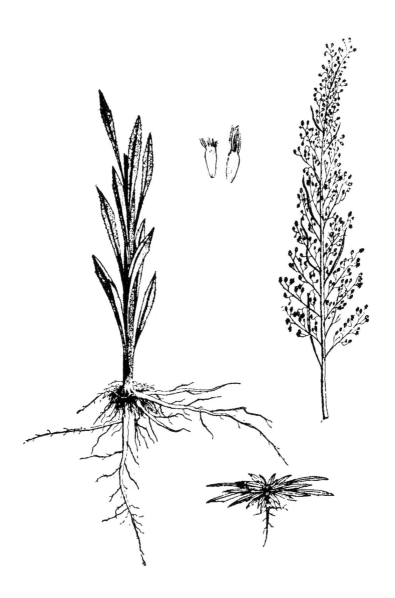

HORSEWEED, marestail, Canada fleabane [*Conyza canadensis* (L.) Cronq.]. Sunflower family. Aster tribe. Horseweed, a native annual or winter annual, reproduces by seed. The stem is erect, 1 to 5 feet tall, usually simple, but sometimes branching at the base. Leaves are alternate, 1 to 4 inches long, bristly with hairs, sessile or short petioled, and crowded on the stem. Basal and lower leaves are spatulate and sometimes sparingly and coarsely toothed. Upper leaves are lance-shaped to linear. The many inconspicuous flowers are about 1/5 inch across in panicled clusters at the top of the plant. Ray flowers are white and almost concealed. Inner disk flowers are yellow. Achenes are numerous, very small, flattened, about 1/16 inch long, with a white bristly pappus. It is scattered over Colorado from 4,000 to 7,500 feet.

BIG SAGEBRUSH, sagebrush, sage *(Artemisia tridentata* Nutt.). Sunflower family. Aster tribe. This native perennial is an aromatic, woody, erect, much branched, evergreen shrub that grows 11/2 to 10 feet tall (average = <3 feet). The densely hairy, gray-green to silvery-blue leaves are 3/8 to 3/4 inch long and usually alternate on the stem. Leaves usually have three blunt teeth or lobes on the end but may be more divided. They are covered with fine silvery white hairs. Yellow, nearly sessile flowers are in a dense panicle. Each panicle is very small and contains five to eight flowers enclosed by numerous bracts. Small seeds are produced in great numbers. Big Sagebrush is found over most of Colorado up to tree line and grows best on deep alkaline-free soils.

FRINGED SAGEBRUSH *(Artemisia frigida* Willd.). Aster family. Aster tribe. This is a perennial, low spreading shrublet that reproduces by seed. Stems are woody at the base but only 4 to 18 inches tall. Several leafy stems are borne basally from a single crown and they are only slightly branched. Stems and leaves have a bitter taste, sage odor, and are white-green in color. Leaves are covered with fine, silvery hairs, roundish 1/2 to 1 1/2 inches long and linearly divided into 3 or 5 segments. Lower leaves are petiolate and upper are sessile. Round, yellow flowers appear in drooping panicles borne in leaf axils. Each flower is subtended by numerous long hairs. Seeds are oblong with rounded edges, flattened and light gray to brown. It is scattered in Colorado below 10,000 feet.

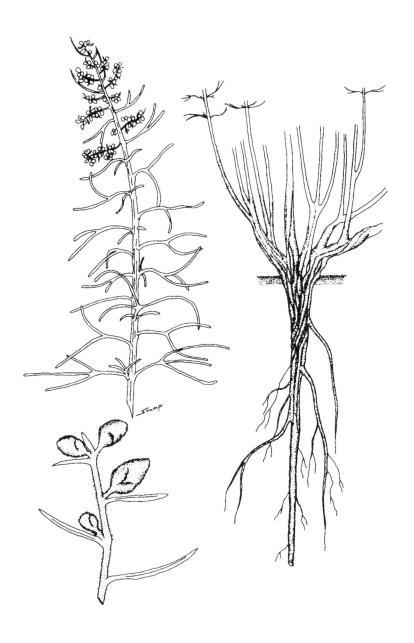

SAND SAGEBRUSH *(Artemesia filifolia* Torr.). Sunflower family. Aster tribe. This perennial woody plant grows 1 to 3 feet tall and reproduces by seed. Fine stems are branched and covered with gray hairs. Leaves are 11/4 to 3 inches long, pinnately divided into fine threadlike segments, light gray-green, and covered with silvery white hair. Flowers are borne on narrow panicles at stem ends. Rounded fruit is borne in upper leaf axils. It has a typical sage odor but is not as large, woody, or bushy as big sagebrush. It is found in the eastern half of Colorado below 5,500 feet.

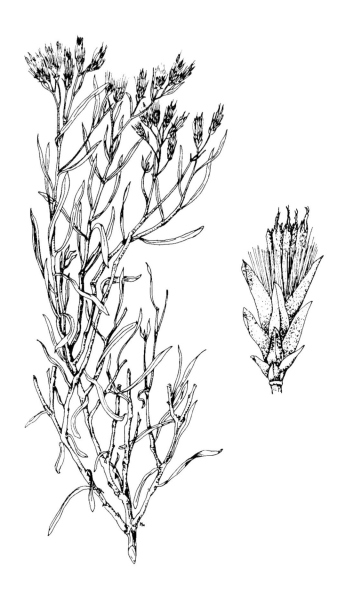

GRAY RABBITBRUSH, rubber rabbitbrush [*Chrysothamnus nauseosus* (Pallas) Britt.].
Sunflower family. Aster tribe. Gray rabbitbrush is a native, strongly scented, perennial
shrub that grows 2 to 4 feet tall. The branches are covered with closely packed gray-
green or white felt-like hairs. Leaves are threadlike to broadly linear, sessile, not
twisted and one to three nerved, alternate, and commonly resinous or aromatic.
Flowers are commonly yellow, terminal, and often compound. Achenes are five-
angled, usually finely hairy, with a pappus of numerous capillary bristles. This is a
variable species in Colorado especially in plant height and leaf shape. It is found on
rangelands from 5,000 to 9,000 feet.

MAYWEED CHAMOMILE, dogfennel, chamomile *(Anthemis cotula* L.). Sunflower family. Chamomile tribe. Mayweed chamomile was introduced from Europe and is an annual or winter annual that reproduces by seed. The stem is smooth below, somewhat hairy above, slender, much branched and spreads to form a bushy plant, 1 to 2 feet tall. Leaves are alternate, 1 to 2+ inches long, fernlike, being once, twice, or thrice pinnatifid. Flower heads are numerous, solitary at ends of branches, 1/2 to 1 1/2 inch across, and resemble daisies with 10 to 18 white, three-toothed ray flowers and a compact center of numerous yellow disk flowers. Achenes lack pappus, are oblong, 10-ribbed, roughened, light brown, and about 1/16 inch long. The plant is ill-smelling with a bitter taste and glandular secretions may burn the skin. It is not eaten by livestock. It is widely distributed in cultivated areas over Colorado from 5,000 to 9,500 feet.

FETID MARIGOLD, false mayweed *[Dyssodia papposa* (Vent.) A.S.Hitchc.]. Sunflower family. Sneezeweed tribe. This native annual reproduces by seed. The stem is smooth or finely hairy, much branched, very leafy, and 3 to 18 inches high. Leaves are 1/2 to 11/2 inches long opposite or uppermost becoming alternate, pinnatifid into narrowly linear, sharply toothed segments. Flower heads are numerous on short stems, 1/4 to 1/2 inch across. Ray flowers are few and inconspicuous and disk flowers are dull yellow to orange. Achenes are dark, four-angled, wedge-shaped, 1/8 inch or more long, covered with fine hairs, and crowned with stiff, brown bristles. The plant is ill-smelling when crushed from numerous glands dotting the entire plant. It is found mainly in cultivated areas in the eastern half of Colorado from 3,500 to 7,500 feet and commonly flowers in late summer.

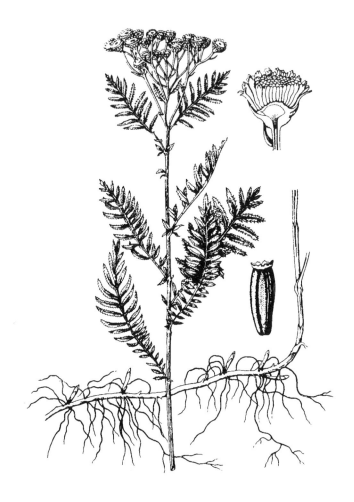

COMMON TANSY, tansy *(Tanacetum vulgare* L.). Sunflower family. Chamomile tribe. Tansy was introduced and escaped from cultivation. It is a strong-scented, creeping perennial that reproduces by seed and short rhizomes. Stems are erect, 1 1/2 to 6 feet tall, stout, smooth, and unbranched except for flowers at the top. Leaves are alternate and dark green. Lower leaves are up to 1 foot long and become smaller toward the top. They are pinnatifid into narrow, pointed segments with toothed edges and are somewhat fernlike. Inflorescence is dense with up to 200 flowers. Flowers are yellow and occur in numerous, compact heads about 1/2 inch across, forming showy terminal clusters. Achenes are brown, small, flattened, about 1/16 inch long, five-angled, with the pappus as a short, five-toothed crown. It grows in north-central Colorado from 5,000 to 6,000 feet.

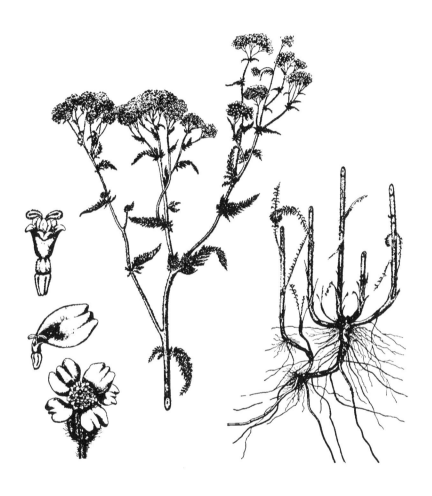

WESTERN YARROW, milfoil (*Achillea lanulosa* Nutt.). Sunflower family. Chamomile tribe. This aromatic, native, creeping perennial reproduces by seed and rhizomes. The stem is erect, 1 to 2 feet tall, simple or branched at the top, nearly always woolly hairy. Leaves are alternate. Lower leaves are narrowly oblong, lack petioles, are 2 to 6 inches long, feathery, finely pinnatifid and hairy or smooth. Upper leaves are less divided and smaller. Terminal inflorescence is flat-topped with many small flowers in dense clusters at stem tips. There are 5 white (rarely pink), small ray flowers and 10 to 20 yellowish, tubular disk flowers. Achenes are flattened, oblong, gray, 1/12 inch or more long, and lacks a crown of bristles. The foliage is strong-scented and bitter to taste. It is sometimes troublesome in lawns in the western two-thirds of Colorado from 5,000 to 10,000 feet.

DEVILS BEGGARTICKS, beggarticks, sticktight (*Bidens frondosa* L.). Sunflower family. Sunflower tribe. This native annual reproduces by seed. The stem is smooth, erect, branched, often purple tinged and 1 to 4 feet tall. Leaves are opposite, at least below, petioled, thin, smooth and pinnately divided into 3 to 5 segments. Segments are lance-shaped or oblong, toothed, pointed at the apex, narrowed at the base, 2 to 4 inches long, and 1/2 to 1 inch wide. Flower heads are numerous, each about 1/2 inch high and usually somewhat broader. Ray flowers absent or rudimentary. If present, they are very small, inconspicuous and yellow. Disk flowers are tubular and orange yellow. Achenes are wedge shaped, flattened, nearly black, 1/4 to 3/8 inch long, and bear two long, downward-barbed awns at one end by which they may readily become attached to passing animals. It is found throughout the Front Range area from 5,000 to 6,000 feet.

NODDING BEGGARTICKS *(Bidens cernua* L.) is similar in most respects to devils beggarticks. The major difference is the achene of nodding beggarticks has four downward-barbed awns.

160

MULESEARS [*Wyethia amplexicaulis* (Nutt.) Nutt.]. Sunflower family. Sunflower tribe. This native perennial, non-poisonous plant reproduces by seed. It is a stout herb that grows from a thick root. The stem is 1 to 2 feet tall and smooth. Leaves are dark green, smooth, leathery, waxy, and glossy. Basal leaves are very large, 8 to 16 inches long, 2 to 6 inches wide, oblong to lance-shaped, and narrow to a short petiole. Stem leaves are smaller, without a petiole and usually somewhat clasping. Flower heads are large and ray and disk flowers are yellow. Achenes are brown, tapered oblong, three- or four-angled, with a crown of toothed pappus two of which are prolonged into stout bristles. It is very aggressive and forms extensive patches from a few square yards to several acres. It is primarily a range weed in northwest Colorado from 8,000 to 11,000 feet.

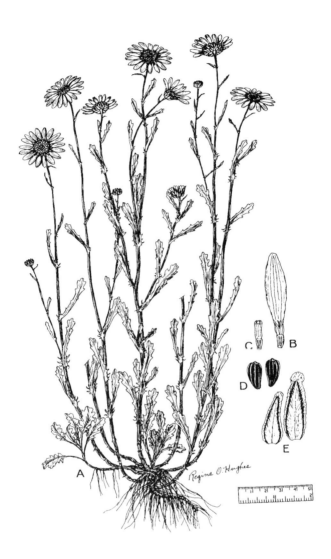

A, Habit —— x 0.5; B, ray flower —— x 2.5; C, disk flower —— x 2.4; D, achenes —— x 7.5; E, involueral bracts ——x 5.

OXEYE DAISY, marguerite, (Chrysanthemum leucanthemum L.). Sunflower family, Sunflower tribe. Oxeye daisy, a native of Eurasia, is an erect, rhizomatous, creeping perennial that grows 10 inches to 2-feet tall. It is glabrous to slightly hairy. Leaves are alternate and progressively reduced upward; basal and lower clasping leaves are oblanceolate to narrowly obovate, 2 to 5 inches long including the petiole, and toothed or lobed with shallow rounded lobes on the margins. Upper leaves become sessile with slightly toothed to entire margins. The inflorescence is solitary or a few long peduncled heads. Fifteen to 30 ray flowers are white, 1/2 to 3/4 inch long; disk flowers are compact and yellow. Flowering occurs from June to August. Achenes are 10-ribbed and lack a pappus. It has escaped cultivation to become weedy in meadows and along roadsides.

162

TEXAS BLUEWEED, blueweed (*Helianthus ciliaris* DC.). Sunflower family. Sunflower tribe. Texas blueweed is native to southwestern United States. It is a creeping perennial that reproduces by seed and horizontal roots. Stems are smooth but may have a few stiff hairs. They are branched and 1 to 2 feet high. Sessile leaves are mostly opposite, blue to gray-green, smooth, narrow to broadly lance-shaped, up to 4 inches long and 3/4 inch wide, with short stiff hairs along more or less wavy margins. Flowers are solitary at stem and branch ends, 1 to 11/2 inches across, with yellow ray flowers and purple-brown centers of disk flowers. Ovate to oblong, imbricated involucral bracts with rounded to abruptly pointed tips subtend each composite flower. Achenes are about 1/8 inch long, four-angled, somewhat wedge-shaped and gray-brown. It was probably introduced in crop seed and is found in north-central, southeast and south-central Colorado up to 7,500 feet.

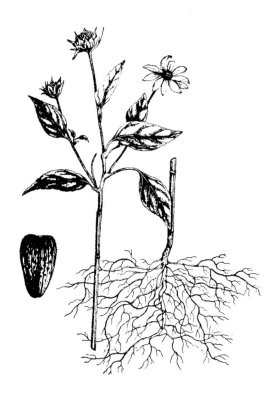

COMMON SUNFLOWER *(Helianthus annuus* L.). Sunflower family. Sunflower tribe. A coarse, native annual that grows from a stout taproot and reproduces by seed. The stem is rough with stiff hairs, erect, stout, simple or branched above, 1 to 10 feet tall. Lower most leaves are opposite but most leaves are alternate, broadly oval, long-petioled, 2 to 10 inches long, somewhat pointed, with toothed to entire margins, and roughness on both sides. Flower heads, borne on long peduncles, are 1 to 6 inches across with large, bright yellow rays, and central, dark purple to brown disk flowers. Achenes are up to 1/4 inch long, oblong, nearly smooth, and gray-brown with a few short hairs at the tip. It is common in Colorado from 4,000 to 8,500 feet.

PRAIRIE SUNFLOWER, plains sunflower, sand sunflower (*Helianthus petiolaris* Nutt.). Sunflower family. Sunflower tribe. This native annual reproduces by seed. It is similar to common sunflower, but is smaller and grows from 8 inches to 4 feet tall. Stems are simple to branched sometimes from near the base. Leaves nearly all alternate, 1 to 6 inches long, somewhat pointed with a toothed margin. and rough-ness on both sides. Usually few flower heads are borne on long peduncles, each is 1 to 3 inches across with yellow ray flowers and reddish purple (rarely yellow) disk flowers. Achenes are oblong, somewhat hairy, and about 1/5 inch long. It grows over Colorado from 3,500 to 8,000 feet. Common sunflower and prairie sunflower hybridize frequently. There are several (up to 9) other species of sunflower in the West. Nuttall sunflower (*H. nuttallii* Torr. & Gray) is a perennial that grows 2 to 10 feet tall. Stems arise singly or in clusters from tuberous roots. Leaves are opposite or sometimes nearly all alternate as they are in common sunflower. There are fewer flower heads than in common sunflower.

SKELETONLEAF BURSAGE, silverleaf povertyweed, perennial bursage, bur ragweed. (*Ambrosia tomentosa* Nutt.). Noxious. Sunflower family. Ragweed tribe. A native creeping perennial that reproduces by seed and creeping rootstocks. The stem is 4 to 18 inches tall, much branched, and somewhat bushy. Leaves are alternate, petiolate, white beneath with minute hairs, smooth, green above, 2 to 5 inches long, and bipinnatifid into narrow, irregularly margined lobes or segments. Staminate flowers are in small drooping heads, usually in solitary, loose, elongated, terminal clusters. Pistillate flowers are usually in pairs in axils below. The fruit is a light brown bur, up to 1/4 inch long, armed with conical spines, and containing one or more achenes. It is common in northcentral, central, and northwestern Colorado from 5,000 to 8,000 feet.

WOOLLYLEAF BURSAGE, woollyleaf franseria, bur ragweed, [*Ambrosia grayi*
(A.Nels.) Shinners]. Noxious. Sunflower family. Ragweed tribe. This native, creeping
perennial reproduces by seed and horizontal roots. The stem is 1 to 2 1/2 feet high,
branches from the base, and is covered with fine white-woolly hairs. Leaves are
alternate, white-woolly on both sides or gray above and narrowed at the base to a
distinct petiole. They are usually three to seven-lobed with lobes or segments being
lance-shaped, and usually toothed with the middle or terminal lobe the largest.
Staminate flowers are in small, drooping heads usually in solitary, loose, elongated,
terminal clusters borne on a stalk. Pistillate flowers are usually solitary or clustered in
the leaf axils immediately below staminate flowers. Achenes are in a small bur about
1/4 inch or more long, with sharp, sometimes curved or hooked spines. It is found in
western and eastern Colorado from 3,500 to 4,500 feet.

COMMON COCKLEBUR, clotbur, sheepbur (*Xanthium strumarium* L.). Sunflower family. Ragweed tribe. This native annual reproduces by seed. It is a large, rough, branched plant, 2 to 4 feet tall, having thick, coarse stems with many brown spots that distinguish it from common cocklebur when both are seedlings. Long-petioled leaves are alternate, triangular or heart shaped, rough on both sides, with more or less wavy, toothed, or lobed margins. Staminate flowers occur in small, green, inconspicuous heads in loose clusters at ends of branches. Pistillate flowers are found below in dense clusters in leaf axils and develop into clusters of oblong burs, each 1/3 to 1 inch long covered with coarse, hooked spines with two heavier hooks at the end. Each bur contains two seeds, one of which usually germinates the first year after shedding and the other germinates the second year. Achenes are black, slightly ridged, narrow oblong, slightly flattened, and about 1/2 inch long. It is weedy many places but is especially bad in sheep country, where burs contaminate wool. Seedlings are poisonous to livestock. It is scattered over Colorado from 3,500 to 7,000 feet.

SPINY COCKLEBUR, spiny clotbur, Spanish thistle (*Xanthium spinosum* L.). Sunflower family. Ragweed tribe. This weed was introduced from Europe or Asia and is common in tropical America. It is an annual that reproduces by seed. Stems are 1 to 3 feet tall, much branched, covered with fine white hairs and armed with yellow, short-stalked, three-pronged spines, each 1/2 to 1 inch long, and arising at leaf bases. Leaves are covered with dense white hairs, alternate, narrow, 2 to 5 inches long, with lower ones being lobed, and upper ones entire. Leaves are white-woolly underneath, and green with white-hairy veins above. Staminate flowers grow in small green heads and form short terminal spikes. Pistillate flowers grow in lower leaf axils and each develops into a bur, about 1/2 inch long, covered with smooth hooked spines and with two short beaks at the apex. Each bur contains two dark brown, flattened seeds. It is found in southeastern Colorado from 3,500 to 5,500 feet.

MARSHELDER, horseweed, false ragweed, giant marshelder *(Iva xanthifolia* Nutt.). Sunflower family. Ragweed tribe. This native annual reproduces by seed. The stem is 2 to 8 feet tall, stout, woody, much branched, hairy above, and smooth below. Long petioled leaves are mostly opposite but upper leaves may be alternate, broadly ovate, 3 to 12 inches long, pointed, coarsely and irregularly toothed, rough above and silky hairy beneath, with the lower ones often being 6 inches long. Flowers occur in small, green heads over 1/8 inch broad in large, terminal panicles and small clusters in leaf axils without peduncles. There are five achenes in each long, ovate, dark brown fruit, each about 1/8 inch long, somewhat triangular, dark gray to nearly black with a ridged surface. It is scattered over Colorado from 4,500 to 7,000 feet and commonly flowers in late summer.

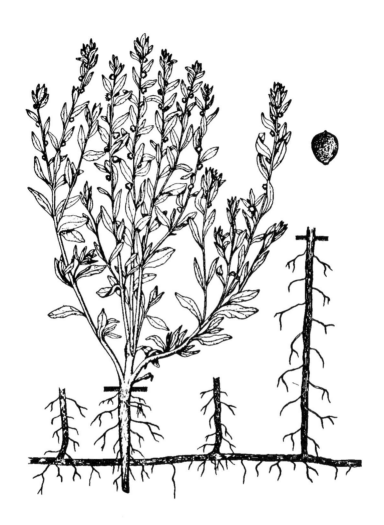

POVERTY SUMPWEED, povertyweed, lesser marshelder, sumpweed (*Iva axillaris* Pursh). Noxious. Sunflower family. Ragweed tribe. This native, creeping perennial reproduces by seed and extensive creeping rootstocks. The erect stem is much branched, 6 to 18 inches high and smooth or slightly hairy and may be slightly woody at the base. Leaves are mainly opposite, numerous, sessile, entire, rather thick, narrowly oblong, 1/4 to 3/4 inches long, rough-hairy, stiff to the touch, with entire margins. Uppermost leaves are usually alternate, nearly sessile, and roughly oval. Small, tubular flowers hang down on short stalks from the axils of small upper leaves. Four to five involucral bracts unite to form a cup with a toothed or lobed margin. Achenes are deep gray to almost black, wedge-shaped, and 1/8 inch long. It is scattered over Colorado from 3,500 to 7,500 feet.

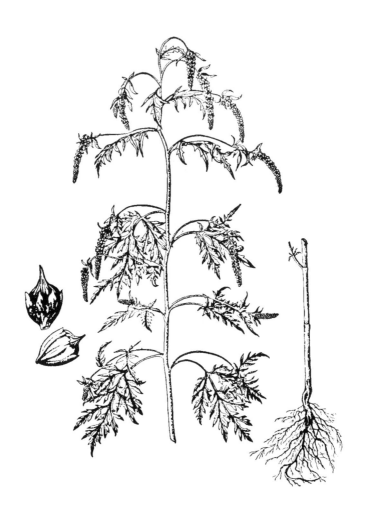

COMMON RAGWEED, short ragweed, *(Ambrosia artemisiifolia* L.). Sunflower family. Ragweed tribe. This taprooted, native annual reproduces by seed. The stem is up to 4 feet tall, erect, finely hairy, and much branched. Leaves are opposite below becoming alternate above, thin, 2 to 4 inches long, once or twice pinnatifid, dark green above, and paler underneath because of fine hairs. Lower leaves are petioled and upper are more or less sessile. Staminate flowers are small, green, in cup-shaped involucres, forming numerous drooping heads, more or less crowded in 1 to 5 inch long racemes on terminal branches. Pistillate flowers are solitary or in clusters in axils of upper leaves. Achenes are gray to brown, about 1/8 inch long, ridged with a beaked crown of five or more points. Its pollen is a common cause of "hay fever" in many people. It is common in cultivated fields, meadows, and on roadsides in the eastern half of Colorado from 4,000 to 6,000 feet.

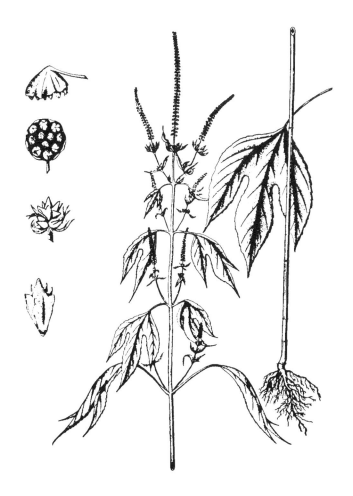

GIANT RAGWEED (*Ambrosia trifida* L.). Sunflower family. Ragweed tribe. This is a native annual that reproduces by seed. The rough stem is stout, ridged, tough, woody, branched above, and 3 to 10 or more feet tall. Long petioled leaves are mostly opposite, large, rough, hairy, usually deeply divided into three to five large, pointed, coarsely toothed lobes, or sometimes undivided, and toothed or the upper ones may be entire. Upper leaves are generally only three-lobed. Staminate flowers are small, green, and occur in saucer-shaped involucres, forming numerous drooping heads that are more or less crowded in racemes about 6 to 12 inches long. Pistillate flowers are clustered in axils of upper leaves. Achenes are gray to brown, about 1/2 inch or more long, and ridged with a beaked crown of five or six points. A cause of fall "hay fever." It is widespread in the eastern half of Colorado from 4,500 to 6,000 feet.

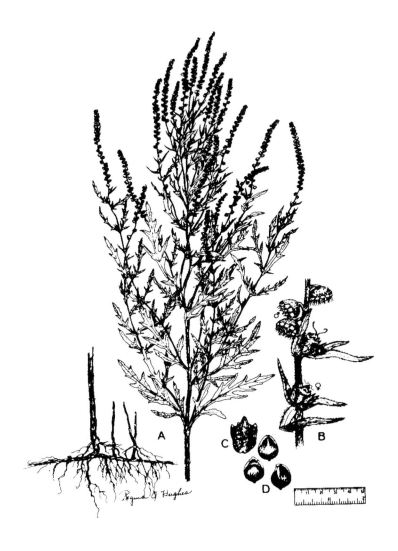

WESTERN RAGWEED, *(Ambrosia psilostachya* DC.). Sunflower family. Ragweed tribe. This native, creeping perennial reproduces by seed and creeping rootstocks. The stem is erect, straight, with numerous branches above, 1 to 2 1/2 feet tall with short white hairs that give it a coarse feeling. Leaves are once or twice pinnatifid, alternate or opposite, nearly sessile, with acute lobes, rather thick, and stiff-hairy. Staminate flowers occur in small, bell-shaped, drooping heads, arranged in loose, elongated terminal or axillary clusters. Pistillate flowers and fruit are usually solitary in lower leaf axils. Achenes are gray to brown, hairy, in a woody hull with a pointed tip surrounded by 4 to 6 short, blunt tubercles. It is found throughout the western states and in the eastern half and west-central part of Colorado from 4,000 to 6,500 feet.

172

COMMON BURDOCK [*Arctium minus* (Hill) Bernh.]. Sunflower family. Thistle tribe. Common burdock, introduced from Europe, is a biennial that reproduces by seed. The first year's growth is a rosette of long petioled, large, alternate, simple and heart-shaped leaves. The second year's growth is an erect, stout, grooved, rough-hairy, usually reddish, much branched stem that grows 3 to 7 feet tall. Leaves are alternate, dark green, smooth above, white-green and woolly-hairy beneath, broadly ovate, blunt, and more or less heart-shaped, with somewhat wavy margins and a stout, hollow petiole. Upper leaves are smaller. Flowers are purple or pink (rarely white) in numerous heads, on short pedicels or sessile in the upper leaf axils or at the ends of branches. Flowers are enclosed in a prickly involucre composed of numerous smooth or slightly woolly bracts tipped with hooked spines. Gray to brown mottled achenes are oblong, about 3/16 inch long, flattened, and slightly curved. It is a serious weed on sheep range where the burs are very damaging to wool quality. It is found in central and north-central Colorado from 4,500 to 7,000 feet.

GREAT BURDOCK (*Arctium lappa* L.). Similar to common burdock but flowers range from about 1 to nearly 2 inches in diameter as opposed to less than 1 inch in common burdock. It is rare in western Colorado.

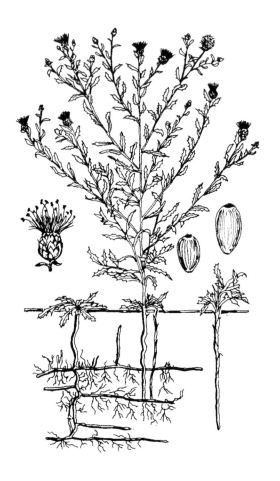

RUSSIAN KNAPWEED [*Acroptilon repen* (L.) DC]. In many cases called *Centaurea repens*. Noxious. Sunflower family. Thistle tribe. Russian knapweed is a creeping perennial introduced from Europe. It reproduces by seed and adventitious shoots from spreading, black, horizontal roots. Stems are erect, rather stiff, branched, and 1 to 3 feet tall. Young stems are covered with soft gray hairs or nap. Lower leaves are deeply-lobed, alternate with the lower most 2 to 4 inches long with toothed margins. Leaves become narrower, smaller, nearly sessile, and with entire margins as they approach the top of the plant. They are covered with short, stiff hairs and are rough to touch. Flowers are thistle-like, solitary, terminal, 1/4 to 1/2 inch in diameter, lavender to white with many rounded bracts with acute, papery tips. Achenes are chalky-white, or gray, oblong, about 1/8 inch long with a bristly deciduous pappus. It is a troublesome weed that is difficult to eradicate. It is generally distributed in the Western States and throughout Colorado, except in the eastern plains area. It is especially important on the Western Slope from 4,500 to 7,500 feet.

DIFFUSE KNAPWEED (*Centaurea diffusa* Lam.) is similar to Russian knapweed but is an annual, biennial, or short-lived perennial with a taproot but no black, creeping rootstocks. It is becoming more common in Colorado. Stems are 1 to 2 feet tall angled, and diffusely branched. Leaves are hairy, rough, small, and pinnately divided. Lower leaves are deciduous and leaves associated with the inflorescence are mostly entire. Corolla is white to creamy or purplish. Involucral bracts are stiff, divided, lanceolate, with a terminal spine.

SPOTTED KNAPWEED (*Centaurea maculosa* Lam.) is also found in Colorado. It is a biennial or short-lived perennial with a stout taproot. There can be one or more basal branching, ridged, silky or cobweb-like hairy stems each 1 to 3 feet tall. Basal leaves are up to 6 inches long. Principal leaves clasp the stem and are sparsely hairy. Upper leaves are entire. Pinkish-purple (rarely white) flowers are solitary at ends of branches. Each flower head is subtended by numerous, broadly to narrowly ovate bracts. Bracts are pale-green and brownish below with a black tipped, pointed apex.

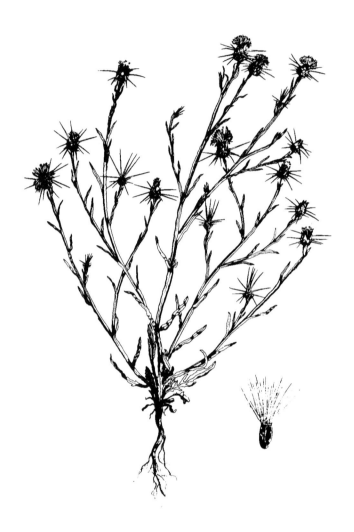

YELLOW STARTHISTLE (*Centaurea solstitialis* L.). Sunflower family. Thistle tribe. This introduced annual or biennial reproduces by seed. The rigid, winged stem is white-woolly, branching from the base and above to form a bushy plant, 2 to 3 feet tall. Leaves are all white-woolly, basal leaves are deeply lobed, 2 to 3 inches long. Upper leaves are enitre, much smaller, narrow, and more pointed. Flowers are yellow, about 1/2 inch across and 1 inch long. They are solitary at the ends of branches and have outwardly pointed stiff, yellow spines up to 1 inch long. Achenes are about 1/10 inch long and of two kinds: light colored with a soft pappus from disk flowers, and dark with no pappus from ray flowers. It is not common in Colorado but is found in the north around 5,000 feet.

176

BULL THISTLE *[Cirsium vulgare* (Savi) Tenore]. Sunflower family. Thistle tribe. Bull thistle was introduced from Europe but is a native of Asia. It is a biennial from a short, fleshy taproot that reproduces by seed. The stem is green or brownish, stout, erect, branched, more or less hairy, 2 to 5 feet high, and leafy to the heads. Alternate leaves extend downward from their point of stem attachment. They are stiff, hairy above, densely woolly-hairy beneath, more or less lance-shaped, 3 to 6 inches long, and deeply pinnatifid. Triangular to lance-shaped lobes are tipped with stout needlelike spines. Leaf margins are bristly. Dark purple flowers are 1 to 2 inches broad, 1 to 2 inches long, and solitary on the ends of branches although they may appear clustered when branches are poorly developed. They are fragrant and surrounded by numerous imbricated, long, pointed bracts, each tipped with a slender, needlelike spine. Bracts are progressively longer and narrower from outside to inside. Achenes are whitish to pale-yellow with dark brown streaks, about 1/16 inch long, oblong, somewhat flattened, sometimes curved, with a long, white, hairy plume, which is easily detached. During the first year of growth the plant develops a deep taproot and a large spreading rosette made up of spiny, lance-shaped, deeply pinnatifid leaves each 3 to 6 inches long or longer. It is scattered over Colorado.

CANADA THISTLE [*Cirsium arvense* (L.) Scop.]. Noxious. Sunflower family. Thistle tribe. Canada thistle, introduced from Europe, is a creeping perennial that reproduces by seed and deep, horizontal roots that give rise to adventitous shoots. The erect stem is ridged, hollow, smooth to slightly hairy, 1 to 4 feet tall, simple, and branched at the top. Alternate leaves are set close on the stem, slightly clasping, very variable, typically smooth, green on both sides, sometimes white-hairy especially beneath, usually deeply and irregularly cut or pinnatifid into lobes or segments and tipped with sharp spines, Upper leaves are smaller and sometimes entire or nearly so. Flowers occur in numerous clusters, each flower is about 1/2 to 3/4 inch across and about 3/4 inch long, usually rose purple, sometimes lavender to white. All flowers on a plant are usually either male or female (dioecious) sometimes resulting in little or no seed production but abundant pappus production, when all the plants are of one kind. Involucre bracts are spineless. Achenes are tan, about 1/8 inch long, slightly flattened and curved, with a white, downy pappus, which is lightly attached. They sometimes blow free in large numbers. It is distributed over Colorado from 4,000 to 9,500 feet.

178

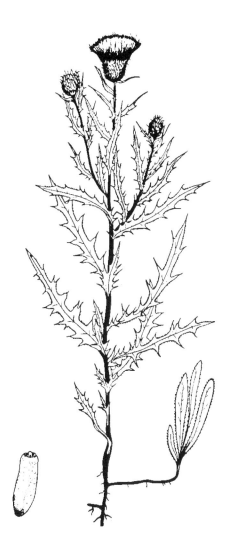

PLATTE THISTLE (*Cirsium canescens* Nutt.). Sunflower family. Thistle tribe. This is a native perennial with a deep fleshy taproot that reproduces by seed. The erect simple stem grows 1 to 3 1/2 feet high, is somewhat angled, and more or less covered with gray cottony hairs. Seedling rosette leaves are entire or slightly undulate and they become more lobed with maturity. The decurrent (downward directed) leaves are 3 to 6 inches long, more or less soft hairy tufted above, densely white-cottony beneath, and deeply divided into narrowly lance-shaped, acute lobes that are tipped with short, yellow-spines. Leaf margins have shorter spines. Flowers are 1 to 2 inches across, solitary on the ends of branches at first and later in leaf axils, and yellow-white (rarely pale lavender). Involucre bracts are linear and tipped with yellow spines. Achenes are about 1/8 inch long, light brown or straw colored with brownish streaks, with a hairy plume. It is scattered over Colorado up to 9,000 feet.

FLODMAN THISTLE [*Cirsium flodmanii* (Rydb.) Arthur]. Similar to Platte thistle but more common in eastern U.S. It is a perennial, reproducing by seed and buds from horizontal roots. The plant is finely, gray hairy throughout and especially so on lower leaf surfaces. Leaf lobes are spine tipped and margins are irregularly spiny. Leaf petioles are winged. Flower heads solitary and terminal on branches. Basal involucre bracts in 6 to 7 rows, dorsal ridges are purple and strongly glandular and tipped by a diverging spine. Corolla deep purple or pink (rarely white). Achenes are amooth, brownish, about twice as long as wide, with a whitish-yellow apical ring, and a white or tan pappus.

WAVYLEAF THISTLE, gray thistle [*Cirsium undulatum* (Nutt.) Spreng]. Similar to above. Perennial without creeping roots and with short, thick, deep taproot. Sometimes reproduces by tuberous offsets. Stem is 1.5 to 3.5 feet tall, erect, and branched. Basal rosette leaves are 3 to 10 inches long, toothed, and hairy on both surfaces. Upper leaves are smaller, toothed and with spines. Flowers range from pink to purple or white. Flowers are sparse compared to Canada thistle. Flower bracts have a prominent, glandular dorsal ridge.

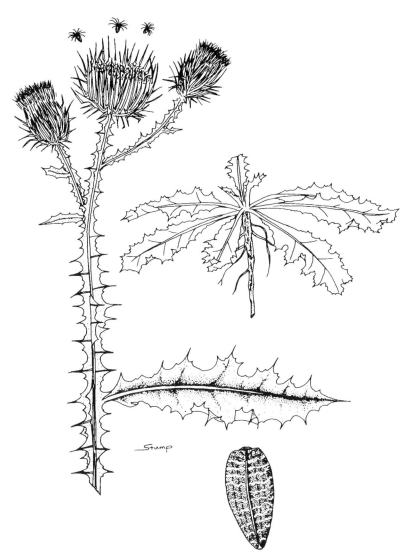

SCOTCH THISTLE (*Onopordum acanthium* L.). Sunflower family. Thistle tribe. Scotch thistle is a biennial that reproduces from seed and is a native of Eurasia. First year rosettes are up to 2 feet in diameter and leaves may be 1 foot wide, coarsely lobed, green with a distinct white midrib. Second year stems can be 8 feet tall (rarely flowers in first year). Upper leaves are alternate, coarsely lobed, densely hairy on both sides and look gray-green. The stem is stout, leafy, winged from decurrent leaf bases, usually much branched, white hairy, and emerges from a large fleshy taproot. Leaves are alternate, coarsely lobed, hairy on both sides and decurrent. Leaves are oblong in young plants and more nearly rectangular in older plants. They have prominent triangular lobes and leaf lobes end in a sharp green to white spine. Other smaller spines are present between longer ones. Numerous disk flowers (no ray flowers present) are purplish to pinkish-white, flat, and subtended by a series of imbricated bracts each tipped with a spine. Achenes are oblong to obovate, four-angled, deep brown to black and distinctly wrinkled. There is a pappus of many capillary bristles which are never plumose. Scotch thistle blooms in June and July.

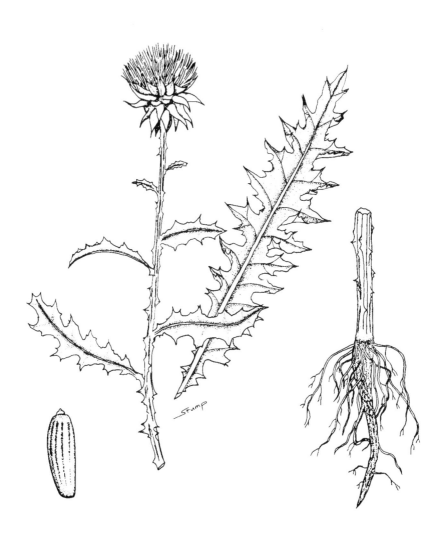

MUSK THISTLE, nodding thistle (*Carduus nutans* L.). Sunflower family. Thistle tribe. This introduced biennial, or sometimes winter annual that reproduces by seed. The first year's growth is a large compact rosette from a large, fleshy, corky taproot that is hollow near the soil surface. The second year stem is erect, spiny, and up to 6 feet tall and branched at the top. Leaves are alternate, deeply cut or lobed with five points per lobe, very spiny, 3 to 6 inches long and extend (clasp) down the stem making the stem appear winged. Wavy leaves are dark green with a light green midrib and mostly white margins. Each leaf lobe ends in a prominent, stiff, white or yellow spine. Flowers are terminal, flat, nodding, 1 ½ to 3 inches broad, reddish to purple (rarely white), and subtended by numerous, lance-shaped, broad, spine-tipped bracts. Flowers are borne on a peduncle that is naked for some distance below the head. Achenes are over 1/8 inch long, striated, glossy, yellow-brown with a hairlike plume. It is an ever increasing problem in Colorado.

BLUE LETTUCE, perennial lettuce, showy lettuce [*Lactuca pulchella* (Pursh) DC.] Noxious. Sunflower family. Lettuce tribe. This is a native creeping perennial that reproduces by seed and deep rhizomes. It is filled with a bitter, milky latex. The stem is erect, smooth, slender, hairless, un-branched except at the top, and up to 4 feet tall. Leaves are alternate, smooth, glabrous, blue-green, variable, 2 to 6 inches long, larger near the base. Basal leaves are deeply lobed or pinnatifid, sessile, oblong to lance-shaped, whereas upper ones become slightly toothed or entire, smaller, and narrower. Inflorescence (20 to 50) have about 1 inch, light blue or violet flowers (different color from other species of *Lactuca*), with each ray toothed at its tip. Achenes are flattened, gray to brown, about 1/8 inch long, club-shaped, with ridged margins and finely grooved sides, and bear a white, silky pappus. It is scattered in the northern and western sections of the United States.

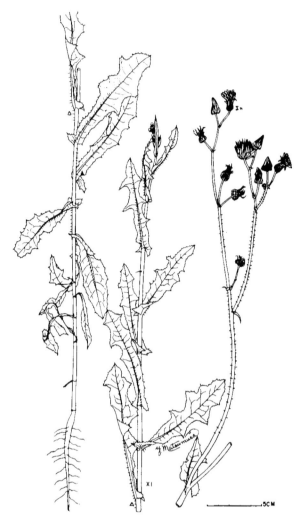

PRICKLY LETTUCE, compassplant (*Lactuca serriola* L.). Sunflower family. Lettuce tribe. This weed, introduced from Europe, is a winter annual, or biennial and reproduces by seed. It is filled with bitter, milky latex. The stem is erect, round, smooth, or sparingly prickly at the base, leafy, branched only in the flowering portion (may be a few basal branches), and 1 to 5 feet tall. Leaves are alternate, usually clasping, oblong or oblong lance-shaped, 1 to 10 inches long, deeply pinnatifid with wavy, prickly-toothed margins, twisted at their base to lie in a vertical plane. Lower leaves are 2 to 10 inches long and may be pinnately lobed or smooth. Leaves are light green with a white midrib closely set with spines on the under side. Flowers are exclusively ray type, numerous (15 to 25), in large open panicles, pale yellow, around 1/4 inch across, on very short pedicels with only a few opening at one time. Achenes are light brown, about 1/6 inch long, 5 to 7 ridged, with white, silky pappus. When growing in the open, it is said that leaves twist so their edges point north and south, hence the name "compassplant." It is widely spread in Colorado but most common in the north-central area from 4,500 to 6,000 feet.

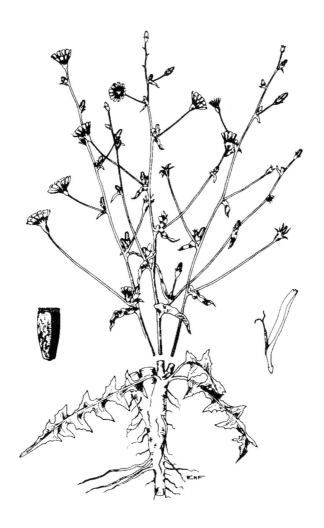

CHICORY, succory, coffeeweed (*Cichorium intybus* L.). Sunflower family. Lettuce tribe. This perennial was introduced from Europe and reproduces by seed. It is filled with bitter, milky latex. The stem is 1 to 5+ feet tall, erect, round hollow, sparsely hairy, much branched, and often becomes purple-red and woody. Leaves are alternate, with the basal ones tufted, spreading on the ground, 2 to 7 inches long, coarsely toothed or lobed, spatulate, and narrowed into a long petiole. Upper leaves become greatly reduced, clasp the stem, and are oblong, or lance-shaped, with smooth or irregular margins. Flowers are numerous, borne singly or in small clusters in axils of upper leaves, on nearly naked or bracted branches, 1 to 11/2 inches across. The corolla is deep sky-blue, to sometimes white. All are perfect ray flowers with each ray five-notched at its tip. Achenes are brown, wedge-shaped, five-ribbed, about 1/8 inch long, and crowned with a pappus of tiny pointed scales. When cultivated, leaves are used in salads or as forage for animals. Many people appreciate the bitter taste of the long tap root when it is ground and used as an additive to coffee. It is widely distributed in the U.S. and scattered over Colorado from 4,000 to 7,000 feet.

DANDELION (*Taraxacum officinale* Weber in Wiggers). Sunflower family. Lettuce tribe. Dandelion was introduced from Europe. It is a deep-rooted perennial that reproduces by seed. The plant has a bitter, milky latex. Leaves are all basal, 2 to 12 inches long, lightly pubescent especially beneath and on the midvein, sometimes forming a flattened rosette, and other times more or less erect, oblong to spatulate and deeply and irregularly cut. The paired lobes or divisions are somewhat acute and rarely entire. The inflorescence is bright golden yellow, 1 to 2 inches across, containing 150 to 200 ray florets. Each composite flower is borne on a hollow stalk, 2 to 18 inches tall. At maturity they form white, fluffy, seed bearing blowballs, about 11/2 inches in diameter. Achenes are gray to olive-brown, 1/8 inch long, ridged, oblong, and bear a silky white pappus. It is distributed throughout the world and over Colorado from 4,500 to 9,500 or more feet.

MEADOW SALSIFY, yellow goatsbeard, wild oysterplant (*Tragopogon pratensis* L.). Sunflower family. Lettuce tribe. This introduced biennial or short-lived perennial is from Europe and reproduces by seed. The entire plant contains a bitter, milky latex. The stem is erect, 1 to 2 ½ feet tall, branched, slender, round, smooth, light green, and hidden by clasping leaves. Leaves are unevenly hairy when young but hairless with age. They are alternate, linear, with narrowing to long-pointed tips, 2 to 10 inches long, and often abruptly contracted above the base and twisted at the ends. Ligulate flowers are solitary and terminal, 1 to 2 inches broad, deep yellow, with a single row of pointed bracts united at their base and equal to or shorter than the florets. The long, hollow peduncle is not enlarged below the flower head. Bracts are about as long as the ray flowers and each ray is five-notched at its tip. Achenes are about 1/3 inch long, rough with funnel-formed pappus that is connate at the base. At maturity, the pappus forms a large, conspicuous, tawny-colored blowball, 2 inches or more in diameter. Flowers open at sunrise and are closed by noon. It is distributed over Colorado, except in the eastern third from 5,000 to 8,000 feet.

WESTERN SALSIFY, goat's beard, yellow salsify (*Tragopogon dubius* Scop.). This is similar to above but somewhat larger (up to 3 feet tall). Leaves are the same length as in meadow salsify but not especially twisted at the ends and more crowded. Inflorescences are borne at ends of long, hollow peduncles that are swollen below the flower. The bracts (usually 13 but may be 8 in stunted plants) of the flowers are longer than the rays, and ray florets are lemon-yellow. Achenes are about 1/2 inch long. It may be more common in Colorado.

COMMON SALSIFY, purple salsify, vegetable oyster, common salsify (*Tragopogon porrifolius* L.). This biennial has a fleshy taproot and is larger then *T. pratensis*, being 2 to 4 feet tall. It has broader leaves, a purple corolla, 2 to 3 inches across, with bracts extending about half their length beyond the rays. The achenes are about 1/2 inch long. It is scattered over Colorado from 4,000 to 7,500 feet.

FALSE SALSIFY, cutleaf salsify (*Scorzonera laciniata* L.) formerly [*Podospermum laciniatum* (L.) DC.]. Sunflower family. Lettuce tribe. An annual, winter annual, or weak perennial with milky latex and a strong taproot. There are one to several stems that branch upward from about the middle. A primary difference from the species above is that the basal and lower clasping leaves are pinnately divided to the midrib and up to 8 inches long. Inflorescence is one to several heads borne on peduncles. Corollas are yellowish and exceed subtending bracts. It is especially abundant along the front range north from Colorado Springs.

MEADOW SALSIFY

CROWNBEARD, golden crownbeard, [*Verbesina encelioides* (Cav.) Benth. & Hook. subsp. *exauriculata* (Robins. & Greenm.) Coleman]. Sunflower family. A taprooted annual growing up to 2+ feet tall. Covered with sharp, stiff, appressed hairs that are often swollen at the base. Leaves mostly alternate, blade ovoid to deltoid. Three+ inches long and up to 2 inches wide, coarsely dentate, especially toward the base. Leaf petiole is a little shorter than the blade. Flower heads in an open inflorescence. The flower disk is ½ to 1 inch in diameter with chaffy involucral bracts and 10 to 15 weakly spreading ray florets. Weakly spreading achenes are not reflexed.

SKELETONWEED [*Lygodesmia juncea* (Pursh) D.Don]. Sunflower family. Lettuce tribe. This native, creeping perennial reproduces by seed and creeping rootstocks. It contains a bitter, milky latex. The stem is erect (or semi-decumbent and arching upward), stiff, round, finely grooved, much branched, 4 to 18 inches high, with a milky latex, and emerges from a tough, woody root. It is often heavily infested with round galls produced by wasps. Lower leaves are linear to narrowly lance-shaped, rigid, entire, pointed, and 1/2 to 2 inches long. Upper leaves become smaller, and the top ones are mere scales making it appear almost devoid of leaves. Flowers are erect, solitary at ends of branches, 1/2 to 3/4 inch broad, rosy pink to light purple. Rays are five-notched at their tips. Achenes are slender, nearly 1/4 inch long, with a light brown hairy plume. It flowers from June to August and is scattered over Colorado from 4,000 to 7,500 feet.

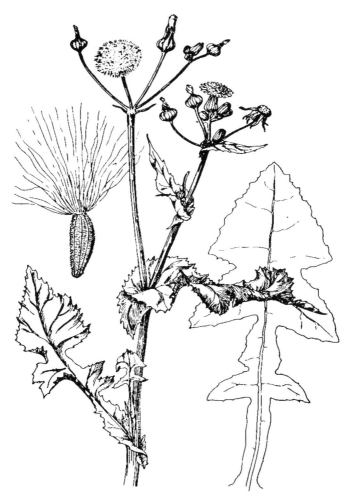

ANNUAL SOWTHISTLE, sowthistle (*Sonchus oleraceus* L.). Sunflower family.
Lettuce tribe. This weed was introduced from Europe and is an annual that reproduces
by seed. It is filled with bitter, milky latex. It looks like perennial sowthistle. The stem is
glabrous, green, somewhat branched, and 1 to 4 feet tall. Leaves are alternate,
crowded on the lower stem, fewer on the upper stem, glaucous, 4 to 10 inches long,
pinnatifid, with the terminal lobe large and triangular, and other lobes becoming
smaller toward the base. Leaf margins are toothed with small, weak spines. Lowermost leaves have petioles while upper leaves are clasping with those near top of plant
sometimes becoming lance-shaped and entire. Ligulate flowers are numerous, pale
yellow, about 1 inch broad, in more or less flat-topped clusters. Achenes are brown,
about 1/10 inch long, slightly flattened, roughly ribbed, with a white, silky pappus. It is
scattered over Colorado, except in the eastern one-third, from 5,000 to 7,000 feet.

SPINY SOWTHISTLE, prickly sowthistle [*Sonchus asper* (L.) Hill]. This is similar to
above large (1 to 5 feet tall). Lower leaves are lobed and quite spiny on margins. Stem
leaves are prickly, clasp the stem, and are not as deeply divided as those of common
sowthistle, or undivided. Achenes have more prominent ribs.

191

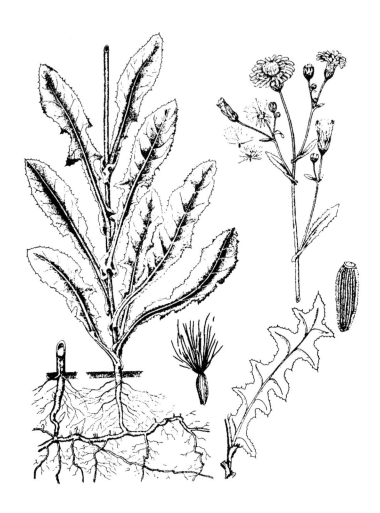

PERENNIAL SOWTHISTLE (*Sonchus arvensis* L.). Noxious. Sunflower family. Lettuce tribe. This weed was introduced from Eurasia and is a creeping perennial that reproduces by seeds and horizontal roots. All parts are filled with a bitter, milky latex. The stem is erect, stout, smooth, 1 1/2 to 4 feet tall, and unbranched except at the top. Leaves are alternate and light green; lower ones are 6 to 12 inches long, deeply cut, with side lobes pointed backward. Upper leaves are smaller, clasping, with slightly toothed, prickly margins; some nearly bract-like. Flowers are bright yellow and 1 to 2 inches across. There are numerous gland tipped hairs on involucre bracts and the peduncle that distinguish this species from other members of the genus. Achenes are small, 1/8 inch long, brown, flattened, ridged, crowned with a tuft of white pappus. It is sparsely scattered over cultivated areas in Colorado from 5,000 to 6,500 feet.

Key to Weeds

HOW TO USE THE KEY

When an unfamiliar weed is encountered, this bulletin may serve to answer the question, "What is this plant?" One way is to thumb through the illustrations in an attempt to match the specimen to a picture. This is an uncertain and time consuming process. Use of the plant key that follows is quicker and more positive.

Use of the key is not as difficult as it may appear, consisting as it does of a series of contrasting choices. The procedure is to follow the choice that applies, disregarding the other one. For example, in the Key to the Groups it is first necessary to decide between two numbers. If the first number 1 is chosen, one has decided the plant belongs to Group A. If, on the other hand, the second number 1 is chosen, one must then decide between the two 2' s. These choices continue until the plant is placed in the proper group.

The proper group having been determined, the same procedure is then followed to arrive at identification within that group, the identification is verified by comparing the unknown plant with the illustration and description designated by the page number. If two or more plants are listed together in the key, final determination will depend upon this comparison, which is much simpler than trying to check the unknown against all drawings in the bulletin. This also is true when difficulty is experienced in carrying the key to the ultimate plant or plants.

Insofar as possible the key is based on characters that are evident at all stages of growth, which, of course, limits use of important characters apparent only at maturity. This key also differs from most keys in that the type of root is a basic character, which suggests the need for a shovel in collecting specimens to be indentified.

As few technical terms as possible are used in the key and definitions of these are included in the glossary beginning on Page 208. Some drawings, which follow the key, explain these terms.

1. Plants with leaves reduced to minute teeth, several to many in a circle around the stem. (Figure 1); no flower or seeds formed -- **GROUP A p. 195**
1. Plants with leaves not reduced to small teeth in a circle around the stems; flowers, fruits, and seeds eventually present.
  2. Whole plants yellow and nongreen, leaves reduced to small scales; plants parasitic on other green plants with no soil roots -- **GROUP B p. 195.**
  2. Green plants with ordinary small to large leaves, not parasitic on other plants, roots in soil.
    3. Grasses or grasslike plants with long narrow leaves divided into a basal part (sheath) that encloses the stem and a flaring or free portion (blade) as in corn, wheat, bluegrass (Figure 2)-- **GROUP C p. 195**.
    3. Plants not grasslike, leaves usually broader than grass leaves, narrow leaves when present not clearly divided into sheaths and blades (Arrowgrass an exception).
  4. Plants not at all woody; perennial or annual.
    5. Creeping perennial plants in more or less dense patches, spreading by horizontal underground roots, rhizomes, or stolons-- **GROUP D p. 196.**
    5. Annual or perennial plants lacking creeping underground roots or rhizomes. (May be crowded stems in bunches or spreading by above-ground runners.)
      6. Leaves, at least those on the lower parts of stems, opposite each other. (Sometimes such leaves are crowded near the base of the plant but are still opposite in pairs.) (Figure 3) -- **GROUP E p. 198.**
      6. Leaves alternate, only one on one segment of the stem (may be crowded on the stems but not opposite in pairs) (Figure 4).
        7. Plants annual -- **GROUP F p. 199.**
        7. Plants perennial or biennial-- **GROUP G p. 201.**
  4. Plants woody at least at the base, shrubs -- **GROUP H p. 203.**

KEY TO WEEDS WITHIN GROUPS

Group A. Leaves in a circle of minute teeth at intervals on hollow, conspicuously jointed stems; reproductive stage unbranched, without flowers or seed, spores borne in a terminal cone (Figure 1). Vegetative stage with numerous slender branches in whorls at joints - Field Horsetail p. 16.

Group B. Parasitic plants lacking green color, not rooting in soil - Dodder p. 131.

Group C. Grasses and grasslike plants, leaves with narrow blades and sheaths enclosing stem at base. A collarlike structure (ligule) made up of a circle of hairs or a membrane usually present at junction of sheath and blade; ear-shaped appendages (auricles) often present (Figure 2 I).

1C1. Stems triangular in cross-section - Water sedge p. 18; Yellow Nutsedge p. 19.
1C2. Stems round or flattish in cross-section, not at all triangular.
2C1. Leaves flattened with edge toward the stem - Rocky Mountain Iris p. 49; Common Cattail p. 45.
2C2. Leaves round or half-round in cross-section or flattened with the flat side toward stem
    3C1. Plants with bulbs at base (like an onion); often odor of onion- Wild onion p. 46; Meadow deathcamas p 47; Foothills deathcamas p 47.
    3C2. No onionlike bulb present; odor, if present, not onionlike.
        4C1. Plants with taproots, (grasslike when young)- Meadow salsify p. 187; Western salsify p. 187; Common salsify p. 187.
        4C2. Plants with fibrous roots, some with rhizomes but none with a taproot.
            5C1. Plants with creeping horizontal parts, these above or below ground, perennial plants usually in dense patches, sometimes in clumps - Arrowgrass p. 17.
                6C1. Ligules made up of rings of hairs (Figure 2 IV) - Ber muda grass p. 32; Saltgrass p. 25.
                6C2. Ligules made up of membranes (Figure 2, I, II, III)
                    7C1. Auricles present on some or all leaves (Figure 2, I) - Quackgrass p.29.
                    7C2. Auricles absent on all leaves (Figure 2, III).
8C1. Stems stout, some leaves at least ½ inch wide - Johnsongrass p. 43; Sorghum almum p. 43.
8C2. Stems not so stout, leaves narrower - Arrowgrass p. 17; Creeping Bent p. 31; Nimblewill p. 31; Reed canarygrass p. 34.
            5C2. Plants without creeping parts (bunchgrasses)), often annuals.
    9C1. Ligule a membrane (may be short-hairy on edge) or absent entirely (Figure 2, I, II, III)
        10C1. Ligules absent - Barnyardgrass p. 35
        10C2. ligules present (Figure 2).
            11C1. Auricles present (at least on some of the leaves) (Figure 2) - Alta Fescue p. 22; Jointed Goatgrass p. 28.
        11C2. Auricles absent.
                12C1. Spikelets (flower parts and bracts) on definite stalks forming panicle (Figure 5).
                    13C1. Some part of spikelet bearing bristles or awns (may be short or long) (Figure 7) - Downy Brome p. 24; Cheat p. 24; Wild Oat p. 30.

13C2. No bristles or awns present on any flower parts - Annual Bluegrass p. 23.

12C2. Spikelets without stalks or on such short stalks as to appear stalkless forming spike (head) (Figure 6).

14C1. Only one spike present (like a head of wheat)-Foxtail barley p. 27; Little barley p. 27; Squirreltail p. 27

14C2. Two or more spikes present (palmate like the fingers on a hand) - Windmillgrass p. 32; Smooth crabgrass p. 38; Large crabgrass p.38.

9C2. Ligules of hairs (for more than one-half the ligule's length) (Figure 2, IV).

15C1. Plants bearing burs - Field Sandbur p. 39.

15C2. Plants not bearing burs.

16C1. Heads dense, spike-like, bearing bristles - Green Foxtail p.36; Yellow foxtail p. 36; Bristly foxtail p.36;

16C2. Heads open panicles; no bristles present - Stinkgrass p. 26; Witchgrass p. 42; Wild proso millet p. 40; Shattercane p. 44.

Group D. Plants not grasslike. Plants perennial with underground, horizontal creeping parts, or with surface runners (stolons), or both, usually growing in patches. (Arrowgrass somewhat grasslike.)

1D1. Some or all the leaves (at least those on the lower part of the stem) opposite each other (leaves may be crowded near base of stem but still opposite in pairs) (Figure 3).

2D1. Plants with prostrate stems, these acting as runners (stolons) and taking root at intervals; leaves round -Gound-Ivy p. 137.

2D2. Stems not prostrate and rooting;, leaves some shape other than round.

3D1. Leaves compound, with two or more completely separated segments (leaflets) (Figures. 8, 9) - Western ragweed p. 172.

3D2. Leaves simple (may be toothed or lobed, but not divided into segments) (Figures. 10, 11, 12, 13).

4D1. Freshly cut leaves and stems exude abundant white milky juice - Showy milkweed p. 119; Common milkweed p. 119; Hemp dogbane p. 117

4D2. Leaves and stems without white milky juice -

5D1. Stems round in cross-section - Stinging Nettle p. 53; Bouncingbet p. 65; Texas blueweed p. 163; Poverty Sumpweed p. 169.

5D2. Stems square or angled in cross-section - Purple Loosestrife p. 103.

1D2. Leaves alternate on stem (may be crowded at base of plants but still not in definite pairs) (Figure 4).

6D1. Leaves compound, with two or more completely separated segments (leaflets). (A deeply lobed leaf is not compound because the divisions are not completely separated.) (Figures 8,9)

7D1. Leaf segments (leaflets) definite and not at all toothed -Hogpotato p. 99; Wild licorice p. 102; Swainson Pea p. 97, Poison ivy p.109.

7D2. Leaf segments, if definite, then toothed or lobed - Poison ivy p. 109; Western yarrow p. 159; Common tansy p. 158; Woollyleaf Bursage p. 166; Skeletonleaf bursage p. 165.

6D2. Leaves simple, not compound (may be toothed or lobed but segments are not completely separated) (Figures. 10, 11, 12, 13, 14).

8D1. Spines present on leaves, stems, or both, these stiff enough to penetrate the skin.

9D1. Leaves attached to stem with slender stalks (petioles), edges not prickly, clusters of hairs radiating from common centers, hence in starlike bunches - Silverleaf nightshade p. 125; Horsenettle p. 125.

9D2. Leaves attached directly to stem (sessile), edges prickly, hairs may be present or absent but not in radiating clusters -Canada thistle p. 178; Platte thistle p. 179; Perennial sowthistle p. 192.

8D2. Spines not present (teeth when present may end in a weak point but this not stiff enough to penetrate the skin).

10D1. Leaves without definite teeth or lobes (Figure 10).

11D1. Leave stiff and sword-shaped with edge toward the stem - Rocky Mountain Iris p. 49.

11D2. Leaves hardly stiff and sword-shaped, if flattened then flat side toward the stem.

12D1. Stems with a collar of tissue (this often papery) surrounding area of leaf attachment (Figure 15) - Red sorrel p. 72; Veiny dock p. 71.

12D2. Stems without such a collar of tissue in area of leaf attachment.

13D1. Freshly cut leaves and stems exude abundant white milky juice-Cypress spurge p. 104; Leafy spurge p. 105; Western whorled milk weed p. 118; Blue lettuce p. 183.

13D2. Stems and leaves without white milky juice.

14D1. Stems soon becoming prostrate-trailing or climbing; leaves often lobed at base and more or less arrow-shaped - Field bindweed p. 129 Hedge bindweed p. 130.

14D2. Stems upright to bushy-branched but never trailing; not lobed at base, leaves never arrow-shaped.

15D1. Leaves somewhat grasslike, all basal, slender, half-round, fleshy, divided into sheath and blade with a ligule between (Figure 2) Arrowgrass p. 17.

15D2. Leaves broad or narrow but never grasslike.

16D1. Leaves narrowed at base to a definite stalk (petiole) - Perennial pepperweed p. 88; Clammy groundcherry p. 120; Smooth groundcherry p.120; Longleaf groundcherry p. 121; Purple groundcherry p.121.

16D2. Leaves without a stalk - Yellow toadflax p.144; Dalmatian toadflax p. 145; California false hellebore p. 48

10D2. Leaves with definite teeth or lobes (at least on lower or earlier leaves) (Figures 11, 12, 13, 14).

17D1. Stems with a collar of thin tissues surrounding them at the leaf attachment (Figure 15) - Red sorrel p. 72.

17D2. Stems without such a collar.

18D1. Leaves with toothed edges but not at all lobed (Figure 11).

19D1. Leaves not at all hairy - Perennial pepperweed p.88.

19D2. Leaves with short or long hairs.

> **20D1.** Leaves whitish from short, tangled felt-like hairs, either on both sides or below only- Woollyleaf bursage p. 166; Skeletonleaf bursage p. 165; Russian knapweed p. 174.

> > **21D2.** Leaves hairy but not whitish from felt-like hairs.
> > **21D1.** Stem leaves remaining broad at base and sping stems (Figure 16) - Hoary cress p. 95; Hairy whitetop p. 96.

> > > **20D2.** Stem leaves narrowing at base, often to a stalk, in any case not clasping stems - Clammy groundcherry p. 121; Creeping bellflower p. 147 Russian knapweed p. 174.

18D2. Leaves with lobes (lobes can be toothed) (Figures 12, 13, 14).

> **22D1.** Stems soon becoming prostrate-trailing or climbing; leaves lobed only at base and more or less arrow-shaped - Field bindweed p. 129; Hedge bindweed p. 130.

> **22D2.** Stems upright or bushy-branched but not trailing or climbing; leaves usually lobed above the base also, not arrow-shaped.

> > **23D1.** Leaves without hairs of any kind.

> > > **24D1.** Plants with strong rank odor of tansy- Common tansy p. 158.

> > > **24D2.** Plants without a strong odor of tansy - Spreading yellowcress p. 91; Purple groundcherry p. 121; Blue lettuce p. 183.

> > **23D2.** Leaves with some sort of hairs present.

> > > **25D1.** Plants with a strong rank odor (of yarrow) smallest and narrowest leaf divisions very narrow - Western yarrow p. 159.

> > > **25D2.** Plants without a strong rank odor (of yarrow); smallest leaf divisions not very narrow - Woollyleaf bursage p. 166; Skeletonleaf bursage p. 165; Russian knapweed p. 174. Diffuse and Spotted knapweed, p. 176.

Group E. Plants not grasslike. Underground creeping parts lacking, may have surface runners. Leaves opposite on stem at least in part (Figure 3).

1E1. Leaves compound, with two or more completely separated segments (leaflets). (A deeply lobed leaf is not compound because divisions are not completely separated.) (Figures 8, 9)

> **2E1.** Stems soon prostrate; leaf divisions (leaflets) small, not over 1/2 inch long - Puncturevine p. 110.

> **2E2.** Stems upright or bushy-branched but not prostrate; leaf divisions (leaflets) often over 1/2 inch long.

> > **3E1.** Fresh plant with very strong, rank, objectionable odor; leaf divisions (leaflets) narrow - Mayweed chamomile p. 157; Fetid marigold p. 157.

> > **3E2.** Plants with little if any odor, divisions (leaflets) not narrow - Redstem filaree p. 111; Devils beggarticks p. 160; Common ragweed p. 170.

1E2. Leaves simple, margins smooth, toothed or lobed but not divided into completely separated segments (leaflets) (Figures 10, 11, 12, 13, 14).

4E1. Leaf margins smooth, not at all toothed or lobed (may be somewhat wavy) (Figure. 10).

    5E1. Leaves (at least some) broad, egg-shaped, or heart-shaped.

        6E1. Leaves without a basal stalk, instead clasping the stem (Figure 16) - Cowcockle p. 68.

        6E2. Leaves with a basal stalk (petiole) (Figures 9, 10) Mouseear chickweed p. 66; Healall p. 137; Devilsclaw p. 146.

    5E2. Leaves longer and narrower than egg-shaped or heart-shaped - Field chickweed p. 67; Mouseear Chickweed p.67; CommonSt. Johnswort p. 76; Healall p. 137; Lanceleaf sage p. 138; Purslane speedwell p. 143.

4E2. Leaf margins either toothed or lobed (Figure 11,12,13,14).

        7E1. Stems creeping and rooting at intervals; leaves round or kidney-shaped Gound ivy p. 137.

        7E2. Stems upright to sprawling but never creeping; leaves variously shaped but not round or kidney-shaped.

8E1. Freshly cut leaves and stems exude abundant white milky juice (like milkweed) - Toothed spurge p. 108.

8E2. Leaves and stems without white milky juice.

    9E1. Plants annual.

        10E1. Leaves lobed (much deeper than toothed) (Figures 13, 14)- Prostrate vervain p. 136; Giant ragweed p. 171; Marshelder p. 168.

        10E2. Leaves toothed, not lobed (Figure. 11) - Lanceleaf sage p. 138; Purslane speedwell p. 143; Marshelder p. 168.

    9E2. Plants biennial to perennial- Blue vervain p. 134; Healall p. 137; Hoary vervain p. 134; Mediterranean sage p. 139; Wedgeleaf fogfruit p. 134;

Group F. Plants not grasslike. Creeping parts lacking. All leaves alternate (Figure 4). Plants annual.

IF1. Freshly cut leaves and stems exude abundant white milky juice (like milkweed).

    2F1. Leaves with margins smooth, not toothed or lobed (Figure 10) - Snow-on-the-mountain p. 106; Thymeleaf spurge p. 107; Ridgeseed spurge p. 107;

    2F2. Leaves with lobed, prickly-toothed margins (Figure 13) - Prickly lettuce p. 184; Spiny Sowthistle p. 191; Annual sowthistle p. 191.

IF2. Leaves and stems without white milky juice.

    3F1. Leaves, stem, or both with short prickles or spines (some sharp enough to penetrate the skin) - Buffalobur p. 124; Crownbeard p. 189; Annual pricklepoppy p. 52; Spiny cocklebur p. 167.

    3F2. Leaves or stems lacking prickles or spines (some have sharp-pointed narrow leaves and some have spine covered fruit).

        4F1. Stems with a sheath surrounding them at the leaf attachment, sheath usually papery (Figure 15).

            5F1. Leaves arrow-shaped; stems often twining and climbing - Wild buckwheat p. 75.

            5F2. Leaves not arrow-shaped; stems upright to prostrate but not twining - Prostrate knotweed p. 74; Erect knotweed p. 74; Pennsylvania smartweed p. 73; Ladysthumb p. 73.

        4F2. Stems without such a sheath surrounding them at the leaf attachment.

6F1. Leaves compound with three divisions (with three leaflets like a clover leaf) - Rocky Mountain beeplant p. 82.

6F2. Leaves simple, or compound with more than three divisions.

7F1. Leaves simple and with margins smooth, not toothed or lobed (may be somewhat wavy) (Figure 10).

8F1. Some leaves (at least the upper) without basal stalks, clasping the stem (hence arrow- or heart-shaped at base) (Figure 16) - Field pennycress p. 85; Smallseed falseflax p. 84; Haresear Mustard p. 86.

8F2. No leaves claspstem at base (may be stalked or stalkless).

9F1. Leaves as narrow as a grass blade or a pencil to threadlike.

10F1. Leaves ending in a bristle or a weak spine; plants never hairy - Halogeton p. 57; Russian thistle p. 60.

10F2. Leaves blunt or merely sharp-pointed, never ending in a bristle or a spine; plants hairy - Kochia p. 58; Fivehook bassia p. 58; Yellow starthistle p. 176.

9F2. Leaves broader than a grass blade or a pencil.

11F1. Leaves whitish beneath from white granules (as if sprinkled with white, sticky, branlike particles) - Common lambsquarters p. 59; Netseed lambsquarters p. 59.

11F2. Leaves not whitish beneath from white granules as above (may be white from other causes).

12F1. Leaves and stems sticky-hairy with some hairs ending in a syruplike droplet; leaves broadly heart-shaped; leaves often opposite on lower part of stem (Figures 3, 10) -Devil's claw p. 146.

12F2. Leaves and stems without hairs or hairs not sticky as above; leaves vary in shape but often narrower than heart-shaped; leaves all alternate (Figure 4).

13F1. Stems becoming prostrate on the ground - Prostrate pigweed p. 61; Common purslane p. 64.

13F2. Stems upright to bushy-branched but not prostrate.

14F1. Leaves (some) broadly egg-shaped or heart-shaped, often over 4 inches long.

15F1. Leaves velvety with dense cover of soft hairs (under hand lens prove to be in clusters) - Velvetleaf p. 79.

15F2. Leaves not hairy or if hairy not velvety with soft hairs (hairs not in clusters) - Jimsonweed p. 122; Common sunflower p. 164.

14F2. Leaves all narrower than broadly egg-shaped or heart-shaped, usually less than 4 inches long.

16F1. Stems branching only at base or apex, not throughout, often single and erect - Common waterhemp p. 63; Kochia p. 58; Fivehook bassia p. 58; Horseweed p. 153; Redroot pigweed p. 62; Prairie sunflower p. 164; Spurred anoda p. 80; Yellow starthistle p. 176.

16F2. Stems bushy-branching throughout - Kochia p. 58; Fivehook bassia p. 58; Smooth pigweed p. 62; European sticktight p. 133; Black Nightshade p. 126; Hairy nightshade p. 127; Western sticktight p. 133.

7F2. Leaves with margins toothed or lobed (Figures 11, 12, 13, 14).

17F1. Upper leaves clasping stems at base (arrow-shaped or heart-shaped at stalkless base) (Figure 16) - Clasping pepperweed p. 89; Shepherd's-purse p. 90.

17F2. No leaves clasp stem (leaf stalk present or absent).

>**18F1.** Stems prostrate; leaf blades round or kidney-shaped - Common mallow p. 77.

>**18F2.** Stems upright (may be branched at base but branches upright or ascending); leaves variously shaped but not round or kidney-shaped.

>>**19F1.** Lower leaves twice divided into threadlike segments giving lacy appearance; plants finely hairy (hairs in small clusters under hand lens) - Pinnate tansymustard p. 92; Flixweed p. 92.

>>**19F2.** Leaves vary but usually not twice divided into thread-like segments; plants without hairs or if hairy, hairs not in clusters.

>>>**20F1.** Lower leaf surface whitish from white granules (as if sinkled with white sticky branlike particles) - Common Lambsquarters p. 59.

>>>**20F2.** Leaves not whitish beneath from white granules as above.

>>>>**21F1**. Leaves once and often once again divided into very narrow, even threadlike segments -Tumble mustard p. 93; Redstem Filaree p. 111; Mayweed chamomile p. 157; Fetid marigold p. 157.

>>>>**21F2.** Leaves toothed or lobed but not divided into very narrow or threadlike segments.

22F1. Leaves and stems with sticky hairs (some hairs ending in a syrup-like droplet or knob, under hand lens); odor of fresh plant strong and objectionable - Blue mustard p. 83.

22F2. Leaves and stems without hairs or if hairs present they do not end in a droplet or knob; odor, if present, not objectionable.

>**23F1.** Leaf surface rough and rasplike to the touch; leaves usually egg-shaped or Wider - Common sunflower p. 164; Prairie sunflower p. 164; Commom Cocklebur p.167.

>**23F2.** Leaf surfaces not rough and rasplike to the touch; leaves usually narrower than egg-shaped.

>>**24F1.** Leaves shallowly toothed or shallowly lobed, lobes not extending halfway into center of leaf - Perennial pepperweed p. 88; Greenflowered Pepperweed p. 88; Black nightshade p. 126; Hairy nightshade p. 127; Jimsonweed p. 122.

>>**24F2.** Leaves deeper lobed (at least the lower ones), some lobes halfway or more into center of leaf - Tumble mustard p. 93; Wild mustard p.94; White mustard p. 94; Indian mustard p. 87, Black mustard p. 87; Venice mallow p. 78; Cutleaf nightshade p. 128.

Group G. Plants not grasslike to somewhat grasslike. Creeping parts lacking (except poison-ivy). Leaves generally alternate, there may be some basal leaves (Figure 4). Plants perennial or biennial.

1G1. Stems or leaves bearing sharp prickles or spines stiff enough to penetrate the skin.

>**2G1.** Leaves long and stiff, saber-like, ending in a spine, no other spines present- Great Plains yucca p. 50.

>**2G2.** Leaves not long and stiff and ending in a spine, or if ending in a spine then other spines present.

3G1. Stems of fleshy, flattened, round to oval sections or joints, bearing long, sharp, stiff spines; no leaves present as such - Plains pricklypear p. 55.
3G2. Stems not as above; leaves present.

    4G1. Stems woody; spines limited to stems - Matrimonyvine p. 123.
    4G2. Stems not woody; some spines on leaves.

        5G1. Stem and leaves exude orange colored juice when cut fresh - Annual pricklypoppy p. 52.
        5G2. Stems and leaves lack orange colored juice - Bull thistle p. 177; Platte thistle p. 179; Flodman thistle p. 180; Wavyleaf thistle p. 180; Musk thistle p. 182; Scotch thistle p. 181.

1G1. No sharp prickles or spines present on the leaves or stems.

        6G1. Leaves compound with two or more completely separated divisions or segments (leaflets) (Figures 8, 9).

7G1. Leaf divisions (leaflets) three to a leaf (like clover) - Poison ivy p. 109; Black medic p. 98.
7G2. Leaf divisions over three to a leaf.

    8G1. Freshly cut leaves and stems exude milky juice when cut - False Salsify p. 187.
    8G2. Leaves and stems without milky juice.

        9G1. Leaves cut into narrow divisions, the smallest one less than 1/4 inch wide.

            10G1. Leaves cut into primary divisions in palmate fashion (Figure 9)- Geyer larkspur p. 51; Low larkspur p.51; Tall larkspur p. 51.
            10G2. Leaves with primary divisions cut pinnately (Figure 8).

                11G1. Leaves once-cut into smooth margined divisions.

                    12G1. Flowers borne on a leafless stalk - Silky crazyweed p. 101
                    12G2. Flowers borne on a leafy stalk - Twogrooved milkvetch p. 100.

                11G2. Leaves cut several times, ultimate divisions toothed (rather than fern-like) - Redstem filaree p. 111; Wild carrot p. 115; Poison Hemlock p. 112; Common caraway p. 114.

        9G2. Leaf divisions broader, smallest ones well over 1/4 inch wide- Western waterhemlock p. 113; Wild parsnip p. 116; Cow parsnip p 116.

6G2. Leaves not compound (may be deeply lobed but divisions not separated as units) (Figures 12, 13, 14).
13G1. Stems with a collar of usually papery tissue surrounding the place of leaf attachment (Figure 15) - Curly dock p. 69; Broadleaf dock p. 70; Pale dock p. 70.
13G2. Stems without such a collar of tissue at the leaf attachment.

    14G1. Plants from underground bulbs; leaves basal, sheathing; fresh plant often with definite onionlike odor - Wild onion p. 46; Meadow deathcamas p. 47.
    14G2. No onionlike underground bulbs present; odor, if present, not onion-like.

        15G1. Stems prostrate and trailing, leaves round to broadly egg-or heart-shaped - Common mallow p. 77; Buffalo gourd p. 81.
        15G2. Stems upright, leafy, with leaves reduced in size upward. Flower heads may be solitary on a naked stem or no more than a few per stem. Oxeye daisy p. 162.

            16G1. Leaves all in a close basal cluster near ground, even in mature plants.

17G1. Leaves with margins toothed or lobed (Figures 10, 11, 12,13,14).

    18G1. Some leaves lobed, without scratchy branched hairs, freshly cut plants with white milky juice - Dandelion p. 186.

    18G2. Leaves merely toothed, covered with branched, scratchy or fine hairs; no milky juice present - Common Mullein p. 142; Moth Mullein p. 142.

17G2. Leaf margins smooth, not toothed or lobed (Figure10).

    19G1. Leaves egg-shaped or oval, over 1 inch wide, abruptly contracted into a stalk - Broadleaf Plantain p. 140.

    19G2. Leaves somewhat grasslike, narrow, less than 1 inch wide, without a stalk or tapering gradually to one; or narrow, fleshy, half-round.

20G1. Grasslike when young, freshly cut leaves and stems exude abundant white, milky juice; leaves stalkless, enlarging at base - Meadow salsify p. 187; Western salsify p. 187; Common salsify p. 187.

20G2. No milky juice present.

    21G1. Leaves narrow, fiat, tapering to a definite narrower stalk - Buckhorn plantain p. 141.

    21G2. Leaves narrow, fleshy, half-round - Arrowgrass p. 17.

16G2. Leaves (at least some) inserted on stems well away from ground level (may be in a basal cluster when plant is young).

    22G1. Freshly cut leaves and stems exude abundant white milky juice.

        23G1. Some leaves lobed (Figures 12, 13, 14) - False salsify p. 188.

        23G2. Leaf margins smooth, not all lobed (Figure 10) upper ones reduced to scales - Skeletonweed p. 190.

    22G2. No milky juice present.

        24G1. Leaf margins toothed or lobed (Figures 11, 12, 13, 14).

            25G1. Leaves densely covered with branched, scratchy hairs - Common mullein p. 142.

            25G2. Leaves either lacking hairs or hairs not dense, not branched and scratchy - Curlycup gumweed p. 152; Canada goldenrod p. 151; Mulesears p. 161; Chicory p. 185.

        24G2. Leaf margins smooth, not toothed (may be somewhat wavy) (Figure 10).

26G1. Leaves white or gray below from short intertangled feltlike hairs; leaves broad, heart-shaped, usually over 4 inches wide - Common Burdock p. 173; Great Burdock p. 173.

26G2. Leaves lacking hairs or hairs not feltlike, usually narrower than heart-shaped, in any case less than 4 inches wide -Houndstongue p. 132; Western stickseed p. 133; Canada goldenrod p. 151; Mulesears p. 161; Broom snakeweed p. 150.

Group H. Plants woody at least at base, shrubs.

1H1. Leaves lobed, dissected or toothed.

  2H1. Leaves pinnately lobed, parted or dissected - Fringed sagebrush p. 154; Gambel oak p. 54.

  2H2. Leaves palmately toothed or divided.

    3H1. Leaves palmately divided, very narrow - Sand sagebrush p. 155.

3H2. Leaves lobed or toothed at apex only - Big sagebrush p. 154.

1H2. Leaves with smooth margins, not at all toothed or lobed.

  4H1. Plants spiny; fruit either fieshy or winged at maturity; neither resinous nor ill-smelling plants.

   5H1. Leaves fleshy, needle shaped, hardly flattened, never over 1/4 inch wide; fruit dry, winged - Grease wood p. 56.

   5H2. Leaves not fleshy nor needle-shaped, flattened, some often over 1/4 inch wide; fruit a fleshy berry - Matrimonyvine p. 123.

  4H2. Plants not at all spiny; fruit of wingless, small achenes; resinous and ill-smelling.

   6H1. Leaves usually over 1 inch long;, achenes with a tuft of hairs at apex - Gray rabbitbrush p. 156.

   6H2. Leaves less than 1 inch long, achenes with narrow scales at apex-Broom snakeweed p. 150.

Figures Illustrating the Key

A	= Awn	Ma	= Main axis (rachis)
Au	= Auricle	Oc	= Ocrea
Ax	= Axillary bud	P	= Petiole of leaf
B	= Blade of leaf	S	= Stem
B1	= Branch of panicle	Sh	= Sheath of leaf
L	= Leaf	S1	= Stipule of leaf
Lg	= Ligule	Sp	= Spikelet
L1	= Leaflet	T	= Teeth
Ms	= Main stalk	T1	= Tendril

Figure 1. Leaves reduced to a circle of minute teeth.

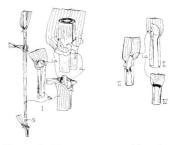

Figure 2. Grasses or grasslike plants.

Figure 3. Leaves opposite on the stem.

Figure 4. Leaves alternate on the stem.

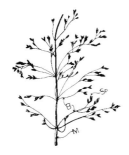

Figure 5. Spikelets on definite stalks (compare Figure 6). A panicle

Figure 6. Spikelets without individual stalks (compare Figure 5). A spike.

Figure 7. Awns or bristles present on spikelet parts.

Figure 8. Leaves pinnately compound. Margins entire.

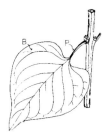

Figure 9. Leaves palmately compound. Margins entire.

Figure 10. Leaves without teeth or lobes. Margins entire.

Figure 11. Leaves with toothed margins.

Figure 12. Leaves with lobed margins.

Figure 13. Leaves with deeply lobed margins.

Figure 14. Leaves with very deeply lobed margins (almost compound).

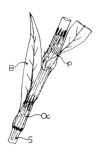

Figure 15. Leaves with a collar of fused stipules (ocrea) at base.

Figure 16. Leaves clasping stem.

Definition of Terms

Achene. A small, dry, one-celled, one-seeded indehiscent fruit.

Acute. Sharp pointed.

Adventitious. Arising elsewhere. Occurring in unusual or abnormal places. For example, a bud that develops in some places other than a leaf axil or stem apex, or a root that does not arise from a hypocotyl, primary root, or one of its branches but from a stem.

Aerial bulb. A small leaf bud with fleshy scales borne above the ground, in the air.

Angled. Sides meeting to form angles or pronounced edges.

Annual. A plant that completes its life cycle from seed to seed in one year. Lasting one growing season.

Anther. Pollen bearing part of the stamen.

Anthesis. Flowering, time of full bloom, time when pollination takes place.

Apex. Tip or end of a leaf, the end opposite the attachment on the stem.

Apical. At the apex.

Appressed. Lying flat against the surface. Often used for hairs.

Ascending. Growing upward or up-curved.

Auricle. Claw-like or an ear-like projection at the base of the blade of grasses.

Awn. A slender, bristle-like appendage usually at the apex of a structure.

Axil. The upper angle where a leaf or a branch joins the stem.

Axillary. Situated in an axil.

Axis. The main stem of a plant or inflorescence.

Beak. A hard point or projection, a firm prolonged slender tip.

Berry. A pulpy fruit with seeds.

Biennial. A plant that lives in two calendar years. The first year is usually a vegetative form such as a rosette of leaves and the second year the plant grows a flowering shoot, sets seeds, and dies.

Bifoliate. With two leaves or leaflets.

Bifurcated. Divided into two forks or branches.

Bipinnate. Doubly or twice pinnate. The primary divisions once again pinnate.

Bipinnatifid. Twice pinnately cleft or double pinnatifid.

Blade. The flat expanded part of a leaf.

Bract. A modified leaf subtending a flower, a flower cluster, or sometimes borne on the stem.

Bulb. An underground leaf bud with fleshy scales.

Bulblet. A small bulb, especially one borne above ground as in onion sets.

Calyx. The outer series of the perianth. Usually it differs in size, shape, or color from the inner or petals. All sepals together forming the outer floral envelope.

Capsule. A dry fruit of more than one carpel that splits at maturity to release seeds.

Carpel. A simple seed-bearing organ or one member of a compound pistil.

Caryopsis. A dry, one-seeded, indehiscent fruit in which seed adheres to the pericarp at all points.

Ciliated. Fringed with marginal hairs.

Clasping. A term used when the basal lobes of a leaf reach partly or entirely around the stem.

Cleft. Deeply cut usually about one-half way to the midvein or base.

Collar. Junction of leaf blade and leaf sheath in grasses and sedges.

Compound. Composed of several similar parts to form one whole.

Corm. A thickened, vertical, solid underground stem. Usually the enlarged fleshy base of a stem.

Corolla. The inner series of the floral envelope. A collective name for the petals.

Corymb. A flat-topped or convex open inflorescence.

Cotyledon. The embryo leaf of a seed often functioning as the first leaf of a seedling.

Culm. The stem of grasses, sedges, and rushes.

Deciduous. Falling away, not persistent.

Decumbent. Reclining on the ground but usually with the tip ascending. Used in reference to stems.

Decurrent. Extending downward from point of insertion, refers to a leaf on a stem.

Dehiscent. Opening by definite pores or slits to discharge the contents. The opposite of indehiscent.

Dense. Crowded.

Dentate. Toothed with the teeth directed outward.

Dioecious. Staminate and pistillate flowers borne on separate plants.

Disk flower. Regular tubular flowers found in the *Asteraceae*. They are the central part of the composite flower.

Dissected. Cut or divided into numerous, usually narrow, segments.

Downy. Covered with fine hairs.

Entire. Margins without teeth or lobes.

Fibrous. Composed of or resembling fibers.

Floret. A special term used in reference to grass flowers with the lemma and palea included.

Follicle. A dry fruit with one carpel that opens down the central suture.

Fruit. The ripened ovary and any other structures that enclose it at maturity.

Glabrous. Without hairs.

Gland. A secreting surface or structure or an appendage having the general appearance of such an organ.

Glandular. Bearing glands.

Glaucous. Covered with a white or blue waxy covering that usually is readily rubbed off. The term is sometimes loosely used for any white surface.

Globular. Round or shaped like a globe.

Glume. A chaff-like bract used particularly for the two lower empty bracts of a grass spikelet.

Granule. A minute rounded object.

Grasslike. Resembling grasses, usually used for sedges and rushes.

Haustoria. Root like attachments of parasitic plants as in dodder.

Head. A dense cluster of sessile or nearly sessile flowers or fruits on a very short axis. It is used especially for the inflorescence in the *Asteraceae*.

Hoary. Gray-white, usually due to a covering of fine white hairs.

Imbricated. Overlapping as shingles on a roof.

Imperfect flowers. Lacking stamens or pistils; compare with perfect.

Indehiscent. Remaining persistently closed, not opening by definite lines or pores.

Inflorescence. The flowering part of a plant.

Internode. The part of a stem between two nodes.

Involucre. A whorl of distinct or united leaves or bracts subtending a flower or inflorescence.

Keel. A dorsally projecting, usually central rib, like the keel of a boat.

Lanceolate. Lance-shaped; several times longer than wide.

Latex. Usually milky, viscous sap. It often coagulates or is sticky on exposure to air.

Leaflet. One division of a compound leaf.

Lemma. The lower of two bracts enclosing a grass flower, above the glumes.

Ligulate. Furnished with a ligule; also used for a strap-shaped structure like a belt.

Ligule. Flattened, usually strap-shaped, corolla in ray flowers of the *Asteraceae* It is also a hair-like or membranous projection up from the inside of a grass sheath at its junction with the blade.

Linear. Narrow and flat with parallel sides like a grass leaf blade.

Lobe. Any segment of an organ especially if rounded.

Lobed. Having lobes.

Monoecious. With unisexual flowers but with staminate and pistillate flowers borne on the same plant.

Nerve. A simple or unbranched vein or slender rib as in a leaf.

Node. The place on a stem where leaves or branches normally originate; the place on an axis that bears other structures; any swollen or knob-like structure.

Noxious. A plant considered to be extremely destructive or harmful to agriculture and designated noxious by law.

Nutlet. A small nut or nut-like fruit.

Oblanceolate. Lanceolate with broadest part above middle and tapering toward base.

Obovate. Inversely ovate, attached at the narrow end.

Ocrea. A tubular stipule or pair of sheathing confluent, elongated stipules. A papery sheath formed by fusion of stipules. Characteristic of *Polygonaceae*.

Opposite. Leaves situated across the stem from each other.

Oval. Loosely used for broadly elliptical, the width over one-half the length.

Ovary. The part of the pistil that contains the ovules.

Ovule. The structure that develops into the seed.

Ovate, Ovoid. Egg-shaped with the broadest end near the base.

Palea. A chaffy scale or bract; the inner of the two bracts enclosing the grass flower.

Palmate. The lobes or divisions attached or running down toward one place at the base.

Panicle. A compound inflorescence with the younger flowers at the apex or center.

Pappus. The modified calyx in the *Asteraceae* that forms a crown of diverse structures at the summit of the achene. For example, the parachute-like structure on a dandelion seed.

Pedicel. The stalk of a single flower.

Peduncle. The stalk of a solitary flower of a flower cluster or of a single flower when it is the only member of an inflorescence.

Perennial. A plant living three or more years.

Perfect. Used to refer to a flower that possesses staminate and pistillate parts.

Perianth. The floral envelope consisting of a calyx and corolla.

Pericarp. The ripened wall of the matured ovary.

Persistent. Remaining attached even after other parts ordinarily fall off.

Petal. One of the individual parts of the corolla.

Petiole. The stalk of a leaf blade.

Pinnate. A compound leaf with the leaflets on two opposite sides of an elongated rachis.

Pinnatifid. Pinnately lobed, cleft or parted, usually one-half way to the midrib or more.

Pistil. The seed producing organ consisting usually of ovary, style, and stigma-

Pistillate. Provided with pistils.

Pith. The spongy center of a stem surrounding or joining the inner part of the vascular bundles.

Plumose. Hairs with side hairs along the main axis like the plume of a feather.

Pod. Any dry, dehiscent fruit, often used as a synonym for legume fruit.

Polygamous. Having bisexual and unisexual flowers on the same plant.

Procumbent. A stem that lies or trails on the ground, usually not rooting at nodes.

Prostrate. A plant that lies flat on the ground.

Pubescent. Covered with hairs.

Pustule. A blisterlike elevation.

Raceme. An infiorescence with pediceled flowers borne along an elongated rachis with younger flowers nearest the apex.

Rachis. The central elongated axis of an inflorescence or compound leaf.

Racemose. Raceme-like or bearing racemes.

Ray. One of the flower stalks of an umbel. Also used to refer to the strap-shaped marginal flowers in the *Asteraceae*.

Rhizome. Any horizontal, elongated stem growing partly or completely beneath the soil surface and capable of rooting at the nodes.

Root. The descending axis of the plant without nodes and internodes.

Rotate. A wheel shaped corolla with short tube and wide, horizontally flaring structure.

Sac. A pouch or pouch-like structure.

Scabrous. Rough or harsh to touch usually from very short stiff hairs or sharp short projections; like sandpaper.

Scape. A naked flowering stem (peduncle) rising from the ground without proper leaves.

Sclerotic granule. Small hard bump.

Seed. The matured ovule consisting of the embryo, endosperm or food supply, and its coats.

Sepal. Part of the outer whorl of the floral envelope or calyx, usually green.

Serrate. With sharp teeth directed forward.

Sessile. Without a stalk of any kind.

Sheath. A tubular envelope usually used for that part of the leaf of a sedge or grass that envelops the stem.

Silique. An elongate, dry, dehiscent fruit with a septum separating into two valves. (*Brassicaceae*)

Spatulate. Broad and rounded at the apex and tapering toward the base.

Species. A unit of classification. A group of closely related populations descended from the same parental stock.

Spike. An inflorescence with the flower sessile on an elongated axis. Usually younger flowers are at the apex.

Spikelet. A small or secondary spike; usually in grasses and sedges.

Spore. The small reproductive body in ferns.

Stamen. One of the pollen bearing organs of a flower made up of a filament and anther.

Staminate. Having stamens only.

Stellate. Star-like or star-shaped with center segments or hairs radiating out from a common center.

Stigma. Part of the pistil that receives pollen, usually at or near the apex of the pistil and generally hairy or sticky.

Stipule. A pair of appendages at the base of the petiole or leaf.

Stolon. A trailing, above ground shoot that roots at the nodes.

Strap-shaped. Long narrow shape with parallel sides and blunt ends.

Style. The usually stalk-like part of a pistil connecting the ovary and stigma.

Succulent. Fleshy or juicy.

Suture. A junction or seam of a union; a line of dehiscence.

Taproot. The primary root continuing the plant axis downward.

Tendril. A slender, foliar outgrowth commonly coiling at its apex and serving as an organ of support.

Terminal. At the top or end.

Tomentose. With a dense covering of matted entangled hairs.

Trailing. Prostrate but not rooting.

Tribe. A taxonomic category placed between family and genus used in the *Asteraceae* and *Poaceae*.

Trifoliolate. A compound leaf with three leaflets as in clover.

Tuber. A thickened, short, subterranean stem having numerous buds called eyes as in a potato.

Tuberculate. Bearing small rounded structures, often pimplelike or rough.

Umbel. A convex or fiat topped infiorescence in which flowers all arise from one point.

Variegated. Having streaks or patches of different color or colors.

Viable. Alive; especially with reference to seeds, capable of germinating.

Whorl or Whorled. With three or more leaves or other structures arranged in a circle around the stem or some common axis, at a node.

Winter annual. A plant where seed germinates in fall and seedlings survive the winter and complete growth in spring of the next season.

Index to Plant Families

Index to Weed Species

Arranged Alphabetically by Common and Scientific Names